D0993099

The Language of Mechanical Engineering in English

Eugene J. Hall English For Careers

The Language of Mechanical Engineering in English

79731

Regents Publishing Company, Inc.

Illustrations by Bernie Case
We wish to acknowledge the generous assistance of Roy Hughson.

Copyright © 1977 by
Regents Publishing Company, Inc.

All rights reserved. No part of this book may be reproduced in any form without permission in writing from the publisher.

Published by
Regents Publishing Company, Inc.
2 Park Avenue
New York, N.Y. 10016

Printed in the United States of America

ISBN 0-88345-303-7 *1-83*

TABLE OF CONTENTS

FOREWORD

This book is one of a series of texts called *English for Careers*, intended to introduce students of English as a foreign language to a number of different professional and vocational fields. The career areas that are covered are those in which English is widely used throughout the world; these include air travel, computer programming, international commerce, or in the case of this book, engineering and specifically mechanical engineering.

Each book in the series serves a dual purpose: to give the student an English introduction to a particular vocational area in which he or she is involved and to improve the student's use of English as a foreign language. This book is not a detailed training manual. It is a broad introduction to the language and terminology of mechanical engineering.

From the point of view of learning English as a foreign language, *English for Careers* books are intended for a student at the high intermediate or advanced level—one who is acquainted with most of the structural patterns of English. The principal goals of the learner should be mastering vocabulary, using language patterns, and improving his or her ability to communicate naturally in English.

These books are helpful with all of these needs. Each lesson begins with a glossary of special terms in which words and expressions used in the specific vocation are discussed and defined. The special terms are followed by a vocabulary practice section in which questions and answers help the reader use these terms. Then these terms are used again within a contextual frame of reference. Each section is followed by questions for discussion which give the opportunity to use both special terms and structural patterns.

Each lesson ends with a review section in which some of the exercises pose problems which occur when actually working in the field.

In this book, the student is asked to identify different types of machine components and explain their characteristics or to describe key features of the engines that have acted as power sources since the Industrial Revolution. Doing such exercises is excellent practice in the specialized vocabulary, general vocabulary, and structural patterns of the English language.

Much successful language learning is not conscious. In offering these books, it is hoped that the student's interest in the career will enhance his or her ability to communicate fluently in English.

EUGENE J. HALL
Washington, D.C.

UNIT ONE
THE ENGINEERING PROFESSION

Special Terms

Engineering: The application of scientific principles to practical ends. An *engineer* is a member of the engineering profession, though the term also refers to people who operate or maintain certain kinds of equipment—a locomotive engineer on a railroad for example. In the latter use, the person referred to is a highly trained technician rather than a professional engineer.

Empirical Information: Information that is based on observation and experience rather than on theoretical knowledge.

Wedge: A triangular-shaped piece of material with one very acute angle. It is one of the simple basic machines used for tightening or levering.

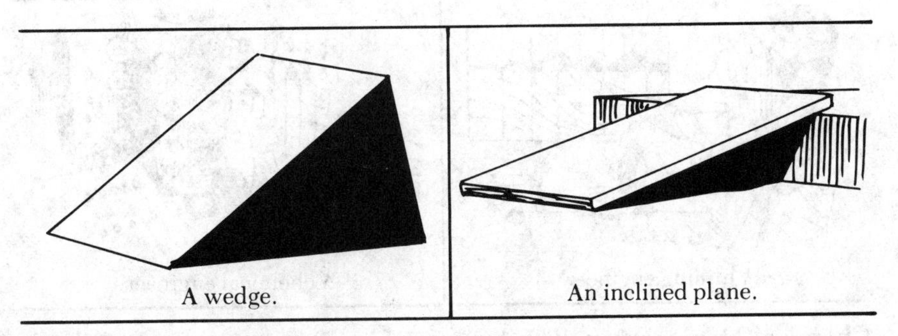

A wedge. An inclined plane.

Inclined Plane: A surface at an angle less than 90° from the horizontal. It is another simple or basic machine used to raise or lower a load by rolling or sliding.

Quantification: Giving numerical values to information.

Horsepower: A measure used in the English-speaking countries for the work performed by a machine. It was devised in the eighteenth century by James Watt and equals 33,000 foot-pounds per minute.

Mechanical Advantage: The ratio of the output force of a machine to the input force necessary to work the machine.

Mechanical Engineering: The branch of engineering that deals with machines and their uses. *Industrial engineering* is a branch of this field that deals with the use of machines in industrial environments such as factories.

A mechanical engineer. A civil engineer.

Civil Engineering: The branch of engineering that deals with the design and building of structures intended to be stationary—buildings, dams, and bridges, for example.

Mining and Metallurgy: The branch of engineering that deals with extracting materials from the earth and refining them.

A mining engineer. A chemical engineer.

Chemical Engineering: The branch of engineering that deals with processes involving reactions among the elements, the basic natural substances. *Petroleum engineering* deals specifically with processes involving petroleum.

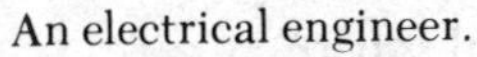
An electrical engineer.

An aerospace engineer.

Electrical and Electronic Engineering: The branch of engineering that deals with the effects and processes resulting from the behavior of tiny particles of matter called electrons.

Aerospace Engineering: A branch of engineering that deals with flight in the earth's atmosphere or in space.

Nuclear Engineering: A modern branch of engineering that deals with the processes resulting from the break-up of some particles of matter.

A nuclear engineer.

Systems Engineer: An engineer who coordinates the work of other engineers from different disciplines who are involved in one project.

Profession: An occupation such as law, medicine or engineering which requires specialized education at the university level.

Vocabulary Practice

1. What does *engineering* mean?

2. What is *empirical information*?

3. What is a *wedge*? What is it used for?

4. What is an *inclined plane*? What can it do?

5. What does *quantification* mean?

6. What is *horsepower*? When and by whom was the term devised? What does it equal?

7. What is *mechanical advantage*?

8. What does a *mechanical engineer* deal with?

9. What is a branch of *mechanical engineering*? What is it concerned with?

10. What does a *civil engineer* deal with?

11. What does a *mining and metallurgical engineer* deal with?

12. What does a *chemical engineer* deal with? Name a branch of chemical engineering.

13. What does an *electrical and electronic engineer* deal with?

14. What does an *aerospace engineer* deal with?

15. What does a *nuclear engineer* deal with?

16. What does a *systems engineer* do?

17. What is a *profession*? Give some examples.

18. How does a *locomotive engineer* differ from a *professional engineer*?

The Engineering Profession

Engineering is one of the oldest occupations in history. Without the skills included in the broad field of engineering, our present-day civilization never could have evolved. The first

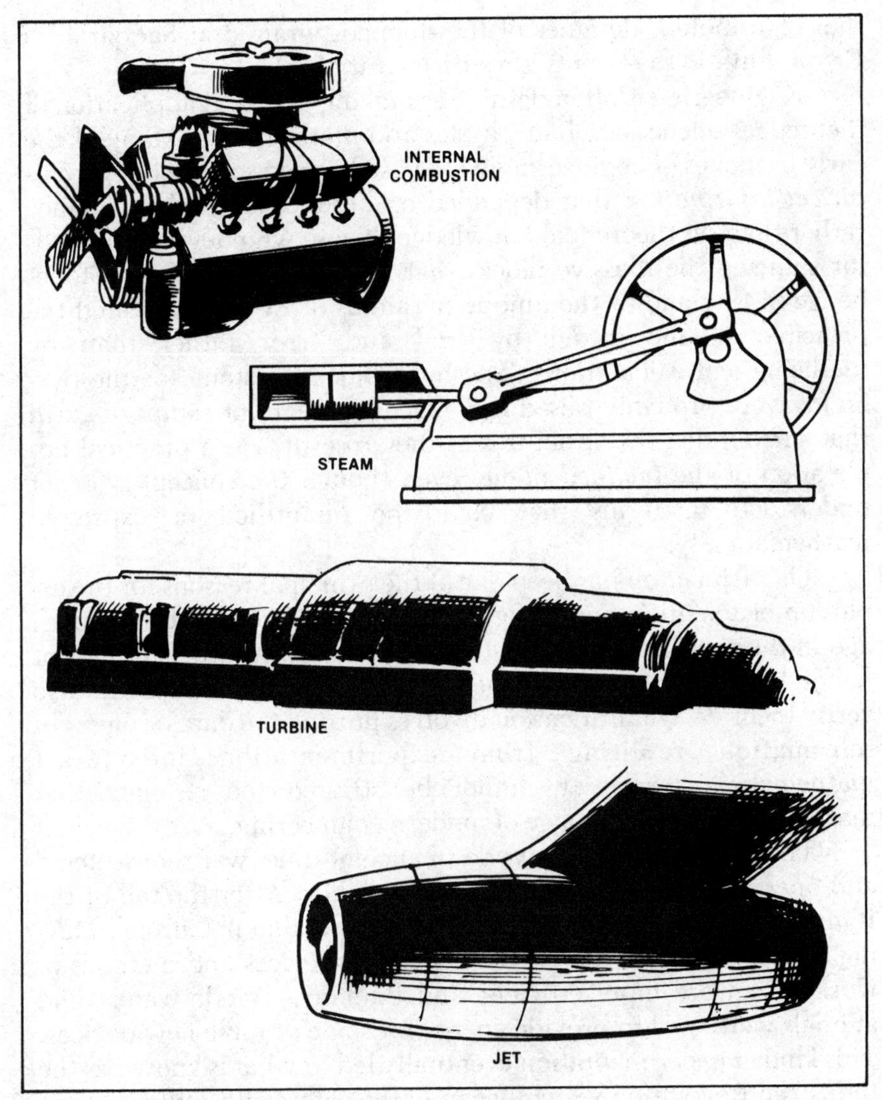

Some common machines.

toolmakers who chipped arrows and spears from rock were the forerunners of modern mechanical engineers. The craftsmen who discovered metals in the earth and found ways to refine and use them were the ancestors of mining and metallurgical engineers. And the skilled technicians who devised irrigation systems and erected the marvelous buildings of the ancient world were the civil engineers of their time. One of the earliest great names in history is that of Imhotep, designer of the stepped pyramid at Saqqarah in Egypt, built in the twenty-seventh century B.C.

Engineering is often defined as making practical application of theoretical sciences such as physics and mathematics. Many of the early branches of engineering were based not on science but on *empirical information* that depended on observation and experience rather than on theoretical knowledge. Those who devised methods for splitting the massive blocks that were needed to build Stonehenge in England or the unique pyramids of Egypt discovered the principle of the *wedge* by trial and error rather than by mathematical calculations. The huge blocks of stone for the pyramids were probably raised into place by means of ramps of earth that surrounded the structures as they rose; it was a practical application of the *inclined plane*, even though the concept was not understood in terms that could be quantified or expressed mathematically.

Quantification has been one of the principal reasons for the explosion of scientific knowledge since the beginning of the modern age in the sixteenth and seventeenth centuries. Another important factor has been the development of the experimental method to verify theories. Quantification involves putting the data or pieces of information resulting from experimentation into exact mathematical terms. It cannot be stressed too strongly that mathematics is the language of modern engineering.

The great engineering works of ancient times were constructed and operated largely by means of slave labor. After the fall of the Roman Empire there were fewer slaves available in Europe. During the Middle Ages people began to seek devices and methods of work that were more efficient and humane. Wind, water, and animals were used to provide energy for some of these new devices. This kind of experimentation eventually led to what is known as the Industrial Revolution which began in the eighteenth century. First steam engines and then other kinds of machines took over more and more of the work that had previously been done by human beings or by animals. James Watt, one of the key figures in the early development of steam engines, devised the concept of *horsepower* to make it easier for his customers to understand the amount of work his machines could perform.

Since the nineteenth century both scientific research and practical application of its results have escalated. The mechanical engineer now has the mathematical ability to calculate the *mechanical advantage* that results from the complex interaction of many different mechanisms. He or she also has new and stronger materials to work with and enormous new sources of power. The Industrial Revolution began by putting water and steam to work; since then machines using electricity, gasoline, and other energy sources have become so widespread that they now do a very large proportion of the work of the world.

One result of the rapid expansion of scientific knowledge was an increase in the number of engineering specialties. By the end of the nineteenth century not only were *mechanical*, *civil*, and *mining and metallurgical engineering* established but the newer specialties of *chemical* and *electrical engineering* emerged. This growth in the number of specialties is continuing with the establishment of such disciplines as *aerospace*, *nuclear*, *petroleum*, and *electronic engineering*. Many of these are subdivisions of earlier specialties—for example, electronic from electrical engineering or petroleum from chemical. Within the field of mechanical engineering the major subdivision is *industrial engineering* which is concerned with complete mechanical systems for industry rather than individual machines.

Because of the large number of engineering fields today there are often many different kinds of engineers working on large projects such as the development of nuclear power or new aircraft. In the design of a new aircraft mechanical engineers work not only on the plane's engines but on other mechanical aspects such as the braking system. When the aircraft goes into production mechanical and industrial engineers are involved in designing the machines necessary to fabricate the different parts as well as the entire system for assembling them. In both phases of such a project mechanical engineers work with specialists in fields such as aerospace and electronic engineering. Each engineer is a member of a team often headed by a *systems engineer* able to combine the contributions made by all the different disciplines.

Another result of the increase of scientific knowledge is that engineering has become a *profession*. A profession is an occupation like law or medicine that requires specialized advanced education; such occupations are often called the "learned professions." Until the nineteenth century engineers were for the most part craftsmen or project organizers who learned their skills through apprenticeship, on the job training, or simply by trial and error. Today it requires at least four or five years of university study leading to a Bachelor of Science degree. More and more often engineers, especially those engaged in research, get an advanced master's or doctor's degree. Even those engineers who do not study for advanced degrees must keep up with changes in their profession and those related to it. A mechanical engineer who does not know about new materials cannot successfully compete with one who does. All of this means that an engineer's education is never really finished so he or she must be willing to continue the learning process.

The word engineer is used in two senses in English. One, as just indicated, refers to the professional engineer who has a university degree and an education in mathematics, science, and one of the engineering specialties. Engineer, however, is also used to describe a person who operates or maintains an engine or machine. An excellent example of this is the locomotive engineer who operates a train on a railroad. Engineers in this sense are essentially highly-trained technicians rather than professional engineers as the term is used in this book.

The systems that engineers produce must be workable not only from a technical but also from an economic point of view. This means that engineers work with management and government officials who are cost-conscious so the engineer must accommodate his or her ideas to the financial realities of the particular project.

The public has become much more aware, especially in the last decade, of the social and environmental consequences of engineering projects. For much of the nineteenth and twentieth centuries, the public attitude could be summed up in the phrase "Science is good," and the part of science that was most visible was the engineering work that made scientific knowledge useful. Countless cars and other mechanical devices are part of our engineered environment.

Today, however, people are more conscious of the hidden or delayed hazards in products and processes. The automobile is a typical example. No one disputes its convenience but many are also aware of the air pollution it causes and the amount of energy it consumes. Engineers are working to solve these problems by designing devices that reduce pollution and improve fuel efficiency.

The engineer, then, does not work in a scientific vacuum but must take into account the social consequences of his or her work. Engineering is described as a profession that finds practical application of theoretical science. A successful engineer must enlarge the definition of *practical* to include the idea that the work is safe and desirable for society.

Discussion

1. Who were the forerunners of modern mechanical, mining and metallurgical, and civil engineers?
2. What is one of the earliest names we know in relation to building?
3. How is engineering often defined?
4. What kind of information were many of the early branches of engineering based on? Give some examples.
5. Name two important factors in the explosion of scientific knowledge in modern times.
6. What made people in the Middle Ages in Europe begin to experiment with new devices and methods of work?
7. What was the historical result of experimentation with different kinds of energy?
8. Who was James Watt? Why did he devise the concept of horsepower?
9. What advantages have scientific research and its applications given to the mechanical engineer?
10. What energy sources have come into common use since steam engines were developed at the beginning of the Industrial Revolution?

11. By the end of the nineteenth century, what engineering specialties were developed?

12. What are some other engineering specialties that have become established since then?

13. What is the major subdivision within the field of mechanical engineering?

14. Why do many different kinds of engineers often work on a single project? Give an example.

15. Who is often the head of a project where different kinds of engineers are working together?

16. What has made engineering one of the learned professions?

17. How has the education of an engineer changed since the nineteenth century?

18. Why does an engineer need constant new learning?

19. How do the two meanings of the word *engineer* differ from each other? How will the word *engineer* be used in this book?

20. Discuss two ways in which the systems that engineers produce must be workable.

21. How has the attitude of the general public recently changed toward engineering projects?

22. The automobile is a typical example of the public's divided attitude toward engineering projects. Discuss this.

23. What are engineers working on in connection with this problem?

24. What concept must an engineer include in his or her definition of *practical*?

Review

A. Complete the following sentences with the appropriate word or phrase.

1. ________________ can be defined as the practical application of the findings of theoretical science.

2. A locomotive engineer who operates a train on a railroad is a ________________ rather than a member of a profession.

3. Law, medicine, and engineering are professions which require specialized education at the ________________ level.

4. ________________ engineering deals with sources of energy and the machines that make use of them.

5. ________________ engineering is concerned with structures and systems that are intended to be stationary.

6. ________________ engineers work with reactions among the elements, the basic natural substances.

7. ________________ engineering is concerned with complete mechanical systems for manufacturing processes rather than individual machines.

8. ________________ and ________________ engineers work with the effects and processes involving tiny particles of matter called electrons.

9. ________________ and ________________ engineers deal with getting materials from the earth and refining them.

10. ________________ engineers deal with processes that result from the breakup of certain small particles of matter.

11. ________________ engineers are concerned with flight in the earth's atmosphere or beyond it.

12. A ______________ engineer often coordinates the work of engineers from several different fields when they are involved in the same project.

13. ______________ information is acquired by observation or experience rather than through calculation and experimentation.

14. ______________ means stating data in terms of exact mathematical equivalents.

15. A ______________ is one of the simple or basic machines; it is a triangle with a very sharp angle at one end.

16. Another simple or basic machine is the ______________, which is a surface that is at an angle to the horizontal.

17. The work that can be performed by a machine can be measured in the English-speaking countries in terms of______________.

B. Here are some projects on which an engineer might work. Indicate which branch of engineering (mechanical, civil, chemical, etc.) would be involved. Some of the projects may involve more than one kind of engineering; if so, indicate all of those you think should be included.

1. A suspension bridge over a large body of water. ______________

2. Finding a new alloy (mixture) of metals that will serve certain special purposes. ______________

3. Designing a control system for the safe operation of a nuclear reactor in an electric power plant. ______________

4. Designing the wings for a new type of airplane. ______________

5. Designing an automatic switching system for telephone direct-dialing. ____________

6. Installing an automated conveyer belt in an automobile assembly plant. ____________

7. Testing the strength of materials to be used in the construction of a sports stadium. ____________

8. Designing and building an experimental model of a mechanical system to generate electricity from the movement of the waves in the ocean. ____________

9. Designing a rocket for space exploration that will use nuclear-powered motors. ____________

10. Designing a process for making plastics from vegetable materials such as soy beans.

11. Improving the braking system in an automobile. ____________

12. Finding a process for extracting a higher percentage of uranium from uranium ore. ____________

UNIT TWO
MACHINES AND WORK

Special Terms

Machine: A device that applies force to accomplish an objective.
Force: An effort that results in change in motion or stress.
Work: The effect of a force multiplied by the distance through which it is exerted.
Block and Tackle: A variation of one of the basic machines; it uses the principle of a lever.
Prime Mover: A machine which converts energy from a natural source like water, wind, steam, or petroleum into mechanical energy or electricity. Most electric motors are *not* prime movers.
Foot-pound: Work is usually measured in terms of foot-pounds in the English-speaking countries. One foot-pound is a force of one pound through a distance of one foot in the direction of the force.
Linear Motion: Motion in a straight line; technically it is known as *translation.*
Reciprocating Motion: A linear motion that goes back and forth in the same path.
Rotary Motion: Motion in a circular path.
Torque: A force which produces *torsion*, a twisting stress or rotary motion.
Efficiency: A machine's ratio between work output and energy input.

Friction: The resistance to relative motion produced by two moving bodies in contact with each other.
Power: The rate or speed at which work is performed.
Newton: The unit of force required to accelerate one kilogram one meter per second per second.
Joule: An international metric measure of energy; one joule is approximately three-quarters of a foot-pound.
Watt: An international metric measure of power equal to one joule per second; 746 watts are equal to one horsepower.
Kilowatt: A thousand watts; approximately 1⅓ horsepower in the English system.

Vocabulary Practice

1. What is the technical definition of a *machine*?

2. In speaking of machines, what does *force* mean?

3. What does *work* mean?

4. What is a *block and tackle*?

5. What is a *prime mover*? What kinds of machines usually are *not* prime movers?

6. What are *foot-pounds*? How much is one foot-pound?

7. What is *linear motion*? What is it called technically?

8. What is *reciprocating motion*?

9. What is *rotary motion*?

10. What does *torque* mean?

11. Speaking of machines, what does *efficiency* indicate?

12. What produces *friction*?

13. What does *power* mean?

14. What is a *newton*?

15. What is a *joule*?

16. What is a *watt*? How many watts are there in a *kilowatt*?

17. What are English equivalents of the *joule*, the *watt*, the *kilowatt*, and the *newton*?

Machines and Work

Defined in the simplest terms a *machine* is a device that uses *force* to accomplish something. More technically, it is a device that transmits and changes force or motion into *work*. This definition implies that a machine must have moving parts. A machine can be very simple, like a *block and tackle* to raise a heavy weight, or very complex, like a railroad locomotive or the mechanical systems used for industrial processes.

A machine receives *input* from an energy source and transforms it into *output* in the form of mechanical or electrical energy. Machines whose input is a natural source of energy are called *prime movers*. Natural sources of energy include wind, water, steam, and petroleum. Windmills and waterwheels are prime movers; so are the great turbines driven by water or steam that turn the generators that produce electricity; and so are internal combustion engines that use petroleum products as fuel. Electric motors are not prime movers, since an alternating current of electricity which supplies most electrical energy does not exist in nature.

Terms like work, force, and power will be used frequently in this book, so it is necessary to define them precisely. Force is an effort that results in motion or physical change. If you use your muscles to lift a box you are exerting force on that box. The water which strikes the blades of a turbine is exerting force on those blades, thereby setting them into motion.

In a technical sense, work is the combination of the force and the distance through which it was exerted. In the case of the box

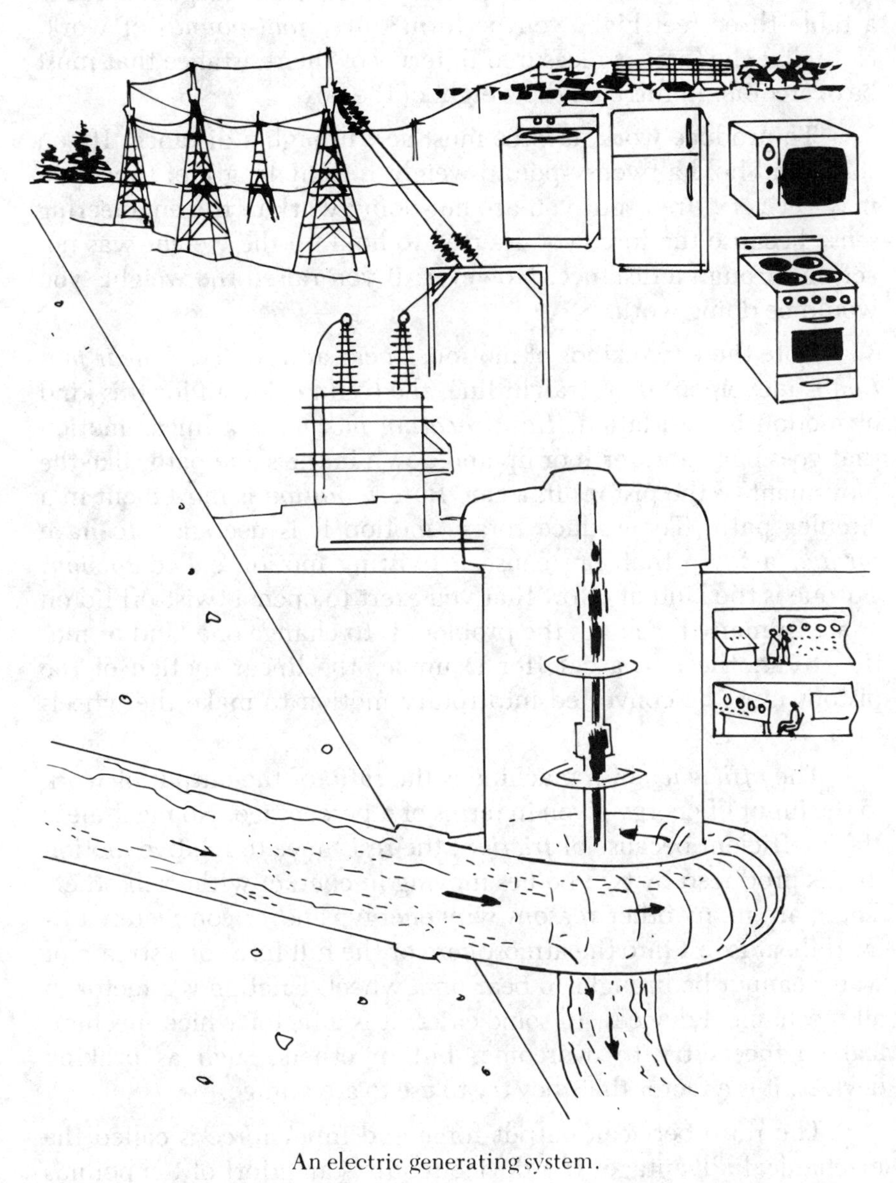

An electric generating system.

that you were lifting, work would be the force times the distance you raised the box. Work can be expressed mathematically in the formula: Work = Force × Distance. If you lift a ten-pound box to a table three feet high, you perform thirty *foot-pounds* of work. Note that the force is measured in terms of the resistance that must be overcome, in this case the weight of the box.

To produce work, a force must act through a distance. If you stand and hold a twenty-pound weight for any length of time, you may get very tired, but you are not doing work in the engineering sense because the force you exerted to hold up the weight was not acting through a distance. However, if you raised the weight, you would be doing work.

Note these two kinds of motion: linear and rotary. *Linear motion* is movement in a straight line; the technical term for this kind of motion is translation. *Reciprocating motion* is a linear motion that goes back and forth or up and down in the same path, like the movement of the pistons in a car. *Rotary motion* is movement in a circular path. To produce rotary motion it is necessary to have *torque*, a force that can cause a twisting motion called *torsion*. Torque is the kind of effort that you exert to open a twist-off lid on a jar. In many machines the problem is to change one kind of motion to another. In a car, for example, the linear motion of the pistons must be converted into rotary motion to make the wheels turn.

The *efficiency* of a machine is the ratio of the output of work to the input of energy given in terms of a percentage. No machine is 100% efficient because of *friction*, the resistance to relative motion that is produced by two bodies moving in contact with each other. There are many other reasons why energy is never completely utilized; heat is lost into the atmosphere or the full force of a stream of water cannot be brought to bear on a wheel. Friction is a factor in all mechanical devices. In some cases, it is a factor which mechanical engineers try to overcome, but in others, such as braking devices, it is a factor that they try to use to advantage.

The ratio between output force and input force is called the mechanical advantage. If a device requires an effort of ten pounds to move a weight of twenty pounds, the mechanical advantage is two. Therefore the mechanical advantage is the resistance divided by the force.

Power is another term used in a special technical sense in speaking of machines. It is the rate or speed at which work is performed. If you raise a ten-pound weight a distance of twenty feet in two minutes, you are performing work at a rate of ten pounds × twenty feet × two minutes, or two hundred foot- pounds in two minutes. Since the rate is usually given in units of one minute, this is a rate of 100 foot-pounds in a minute.

In the English-speaking countries, the rate of doing work is usually given in terms of horsepower, often abbreviated hp. You will remember that this expression resulted from the desire of the inventor James Watt to describe the work his steam engines performed in terms that his customers could easily understand. After much experimentation, he settled on a rate of 33,000 foot-pounds per minute as one horsepower.

In the metric system power is measured in terms of *watts* and *kilowatts*. The watt is the power to do one *joule* of work per second. The joule is a small unit of work, approximately three-quarters of a foot-pound. One horsepower is equal to 746 watts. The kilowatt, a more widely used term, equals a thousand watts or approximately 1⅓ horsepower in the English system. The *newton* is a unit equal to the force necessary to accelerate one kilogram one meter per second per second.

We are used to hearing the words watt and kilowatt in connection with electricity but we must remember that from a scientific viewpoint any kind of power can be quantified in the same terms. It is the work rather than the source of energy which is important; watts and kilowatts are used to measure power that results from mechanical as well as electrical energy.

Discussion

1. What is a simple definition of a machine? What is a more technical definition? What does this definition imply?

2. Describe some very simple machines. What are some complex ones? Give examples of your own.

3. What are the output and input of a machine?

4. What are the machines called whose input is a natural source of energy? What are some natural sources of energy and the machines that use them?

5. Why aren't electric motors prime movers?

6. What is force in a technical sense? Give some examples.

7. How can work be expressed mathematically? Give an example.

8. In what way must a force be acting to produce work? Give examples. What kind of effort would not produce work?

9. What are the two principal kinds of motion?

10. Which kind of motion is reciprocating motion? What is its principal characteristic?

11. What is torsion? What is necessary to produce it? What is necessary to produce rotary motion?

12. What is an important problem in many machines? Give an example.

13. Why is no machine 100% efficient?

14. What are some other reasons why energy is never completely utilized?

15. How do mechanical engineers deal with the factor of friction?

16. What is the ratio between a machine's output and input? Give an example.

17. In a technical sense, what does power define? Give an example.

18. How is the rate of doing work usually given in the English-speaking countries? Why was the term invented? What does it equal?

19. In what terms is power measured in the metric system?

20. What do the joule, the watt, the kilowatt, and the newton approximately equal in the English system?

21. Why can the terms watt and kilowatt be used to refer to mechanical as well as electrical energy?

Review

A. Match the terms on the left with the statements on the right.

1. Force	____The ratio between output in work and input in energy.
2. Work	____The resistance to motion produced by two bodies that are moving in contact with each other.
3. Machine	____Motion in a straight line, or linear motion.
4. Prime Mover	____An English measure of power equal to 33,000 foot-pounds per minute.
5. Translation	____A twisting force that produces torsion or rotary motion.
6. Reciprocating Motion	____The ratio of output force to input force of a machine.
7. Rotary Motion	____A metric measure of power, equal to one joule per second.
8. Torque	____An English measure of work, a force of one pound moving through a distance of one foot in the direction of the force.

9. Efficiency ____An effort that results in motion or physical change.

10. Mechanical Advantage ____Force necessary to move one kilogram one meter per second per second.

11. Friction ____Force times the distance through which it is exerted.

12. Power ____A metric measure of energy, equal to approximately ¾ of a foot-pound.

13. Foot-pound ____A device that applies force to accomplish an objective.

14. Horsepower ____The strength or force at which work is performed.

15. Joule ____A machine that converts energy from a natural source.

16. Watt ____A metric measure of power, equal to a thousand watts, or approximately 1⅓ hp. in the English system.

17. Kilowatt ____Motion in a circular path.

18. Newton ____Back and forth or up and down motion in a straight line.

B. Figure out the work in foot-pounds.

1. Force - 8 pounds Distance - 9 feet

2. Force - 12 pounds Distance - 6 feet

3. Force - 200 pounds Distance - 10 feet

4. Force - 900 pounds Distance - 5½ feet

5. Force - 3,000 pounds   Distance - 60 feet

C. Find the mechanical advantage.

1. Resistance - 90 pounds   Force - 30 pounds
2. Resistance - 90 pounds   Force - 45 pounds
3. Resistance - 90 pounds   Force - 15 pounds
4. Resistance - 20 pounds   Force - 5 pounds
5. Resistance - 100 pounds   Force - 20 pounds

D. Compute the power in foot-pounds per minute.

1. Force - 10 pounds   Distance - 30 feet   Time - 3 minutes
2. Force - 8 pounds   Distance - 40 feet   Time - ½ minute
3. Force - 50 pounds   Distance - 10 feet   Time - 10 minutes
4. Force - 200 pounds   Distance - 20 feet   Time - 8 minutes
5. Force - 900 pounds   Distance - 3 feet   Time - 9 minutes

UNIT THREE
THE BASIC MACHINES

Special Terms

Lever: A basic machine consisting of a rigid piece or bar that turns on a point.

Fulcrum: The point on which a lever turns.

Effort End: The point where force is applied to a lever.

Load End: The point where there is resisting force on a lever.

A lever.

Wheel and Axle: A basic machine consisting of a wheel that rotates on a shaft called the axle.

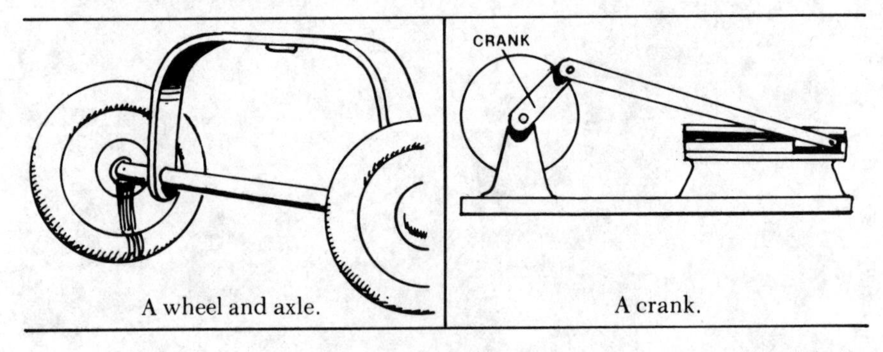

A wheel and axle.

A crank.

Crank: A bent shaft or arm for transmitting motion or changing from rotary to reciprocating motion and vice versa.

Pulley: A basic machine consisting of a wheel with a grooved rim through which a rope, wire, or chain is passed.

Block: A pulley contained in a housing; the combination of a fixed and a movable block together with a rope is known as a *block and tackle.*

Wedge: A basic machine consisting of a piece of material tapering to a thin edge.

Inclined Plane: A basic machine; at its simplest a surface at an angle to the horizon.

Screw: A basic machine sometimes described as a helical inclined plane or a cylinder with a helical groove around the outer surface.

Helix: The corkscrew-shaped figure that results from wrapping the line of an inclined plane around a cylinder; the plural is *helices.*

Jack: A device used to raise heavy weights for short distances.

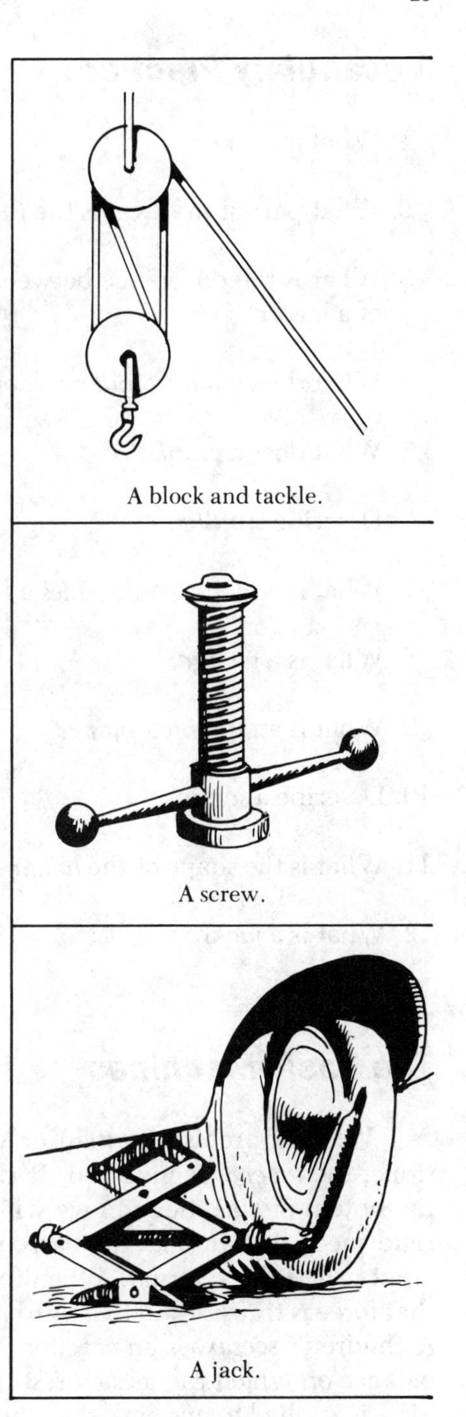

A block and tackle.

A screw.

A jack.

Vocabulary Practice

1. What is a *lever*?

2. What part of the lever is the *fulcrum*?

3. What is the difference between the *effort end* and the *load end* of a lever?

4. What does a *wheel and axle* consist of?

5. What does a *crank* do?

6. Describe a *pulley*.

7. What is a *block*? What does a *block and tackle* consist of?

8. What is a *wedge*?

9. What is an *inclined plane*?

10. Describe a *screw*.

11. What is the shape of the *helix*?

12. What is a *jack*?

The Basic Machines

When a prehistoric man or woman used a stick to pry up a stone, the *lever* was invented. It is one of the six basic machines in the system of classification we will follow in this book. A lever is a rigid piece or bar, like the early person's stick, which turns on a point called the *fulcrum*. When force is applied at a second point, that force is transmitted to a third point where it can perform work. A children's seesaw is an excellent example of a lever. The point of balance on which the seesaw rests is the fulcrum; when downward force is applied to one end, the other end rises.

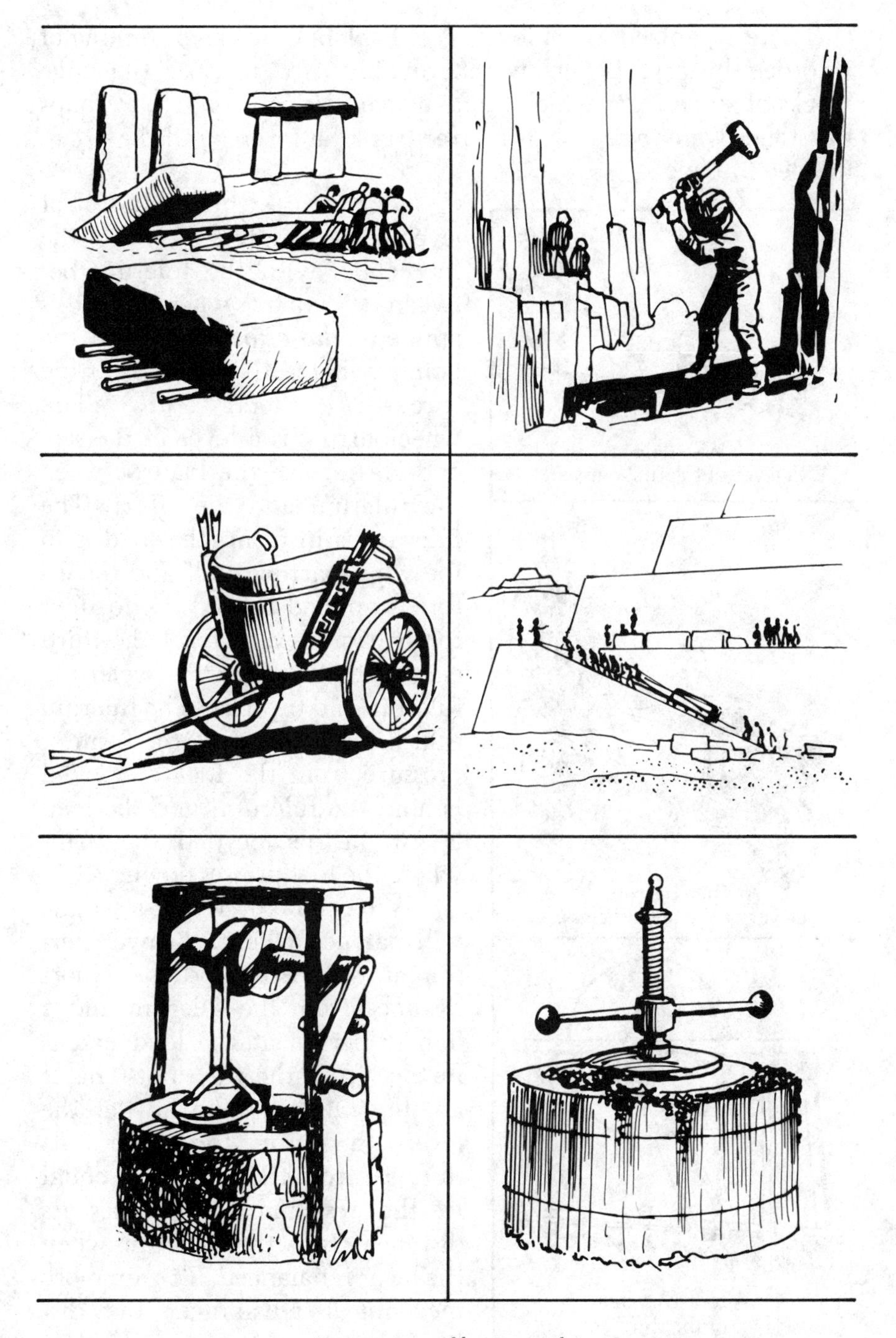

Ancient uses of basic machines.

The organized use of levers goes back beyond the beginning of recorded history. Levers were probably used to raise the huge blocks of stone from which Stone-henge was constructed. Perhaps the stones were raised by using tree trunks as levers until the stones toppled into place.

A seesaw—
a lever of the first class.

A wheelbarrow—
a lever of the second class.

A foot-treadle—
a lever of the third class.

There are three classes of levers. The seesaw is a lever of the first class, with the fulcrum between the point where force is applied—*the effort end*—and the point where there is resisting force—*the load end.* The wheelbarrow is a lever of the second class, with the load between the fulcrum and the effort. The fulcrum is in front, the load is in the wheelbarrow itself and the effort is applied behind the load. A foot-treadle is a lever of the third class with the effort between the fulcrum and the load. The fulcrum is at one end, force in the form of pressure from the foot is applied behind the fulcrum, and the load is still farther beyond the point where the foot presses down.

We can observe that a seesaw will balance when a heavier person at the effort end is a short distance from the fulcrum and a lighter person at the load end is farther from the fulcrum. This is an illustration of the law of the lever: the effort force times its distance from the fulcrum is equal to the resisting force times its distance from the fulcrum when the lever is balanced. To gain more mechanical advantage, the distance between the point of effort and the fulcrum can be lengthened so that the effort is exerted through a greater distance. The fulcrum must exert an upward force equal to the two downward forces exerted on it—the downward force required to lower the effort arm and the downward force of the load.

The *wheel and axle* is the second basic type of machine. Like the lever, the wheel goes back to prehistoric times when someone probably discovered that it was easier to move heavy weights by sliding them on logs than by carrying them. The axle is a shaft on which a wheel can turn and the wheel and axle combination may have first been used sometime around 3,000 B.C. for water-raising devices. Its use for transportation evolved with the domestication of the horse. War chariots were the tanks of ancient times and wagons were the trucks.

In addition to its uses for transportation the wheel has endless applications. An early and important one was for the potter's wheel which permitted craftspeople to shape clay into controlled thickness for greater variety of forms and uses. Wheels were also put to work early for irrigation by raising water from streams or wells to divert it into artificial channels. Other early uses were for millstones to grind grain and for waterwheels that could transmit energy for many purposes.

The potential of the wheel was increased by the development of the *crank*. The crank is a device which can transmit motion or can change rotary motion into reciprocating motion and the reverse. With the development of the crank, waterwheels could be put to work for essential purposes such as crushing rock or sawing wood.

A simple pulley.

The third basic machine is the *pulley*. In its simplest form it consists of a wheel with a groove around its outer surface through which a rope, wire, or chain can be passed. This simple device was used in ancient times for tasks such as raising water from wells or streams and hoisting sails onto ships. A pulley contained in a housing is called a *block*. When a fixed block is used with a movable block to which a weight is attached, downward pull on the rope will raise the weight. This device is called a *block and tackle.*

The block and tackle illustrated has a mechanical advantage of two. The mechanical advantage can be increased by different arrangements and combinations of blocks.

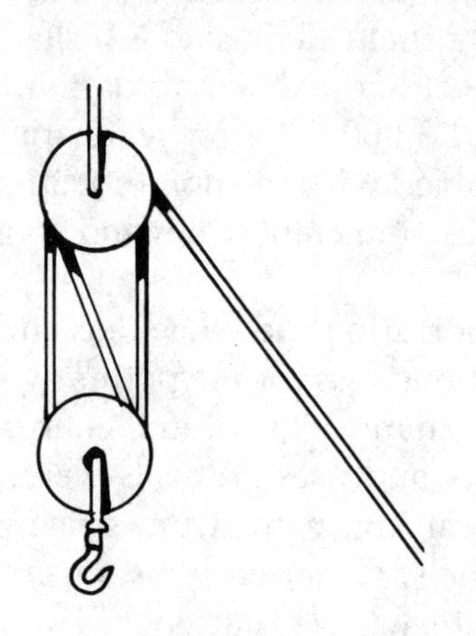

A block and tackle with the mechanical advantage of two.

A pulley as a lever of the second class.

The movable pulley acts on the leverage principle; it forms a lever of the second class (like the wheelbarrow) with the fulcrum at the downward point of contact of rope and wheel, the load suspended from the axle, and the effort at the upward point of contact of rope and wheel. Increasing the number of fixed and movable pulleys increases the mechanical advantage.

The three remaining basic machines are so related to one another that they are sometimes grouped together. They are the *wedge*, the *inclined plane*, and the *screw*.

The wedge is a triangle with two chief surfaces that meet in a sharp angle or taper to a thin edge. Wedges are used for splitting open or pushing apart. They were used from very early times for such purposes as quarrying rock, plowing fields or cutting wood, as with an axe. A nail is a familiar form of the wedge.

The mechanical advantage of a wedge can be computed by dividing the length of the surface by the breadth of the wedge. A wedge twelve inches long with a breadth of three inches would have a theoretical mechanical advantage of four. However, friction is an important consideration in use of the wedge; in reality much of the advantage is lost. In fact, it is friction that holds a nail in place.

We have already mentioned the inclined plane as the probable method employed by the Egyptians for manipulating into place the huge blocks of stone in the pyramids. Early men and women knew that a weight could be pushed up a hill or a ramp of earth with less effort than would be required to move the same weight vertically. Many centuries had to pass before it was discovered that this mechanical device could be explained mathematically. The effort put forth in moving a load up an inclined plane is the same as the proportion between the height of the rise and the length of the inclined plane. If the rise is five feet and the length of the plane is twenty feet, the ratio is one to four. Therefore an effort equal to one-quarter of the load would theoretically be needed to raise the load. In actual practice, friction has to be overcome so a greater effort is required.

The inclined plane is an important factor that concerns civil engineers when designing highways or railroads. The mechanical engineer more frequently uses the screw, a spiral form of the inclined plane. The figure that results from wrapping the line of an inclined plane around a cylinder is called a *helix*.

The screw was used in ancient times to press grapes for wine or olives for oil. In the Middle Ages it was important in the development of printing. Today we are most familiar with the screw as a fastener but it has numerous other uses. It is one of the most important devices for amplifying or increasing force. A familiar adaptation is the screw *jack* used to lift automobiles or any great weight through a short distance. The screw is also a major means of changing the direction of motion.

Both the screw and the helix have so many adaptations in modern machines that it is impossible to list them but one in particular is extremely interesting: the helical motion of a propeller on a boat or an airplane moves the vessel or plane ahead as though it were screwing its way through the water or air!

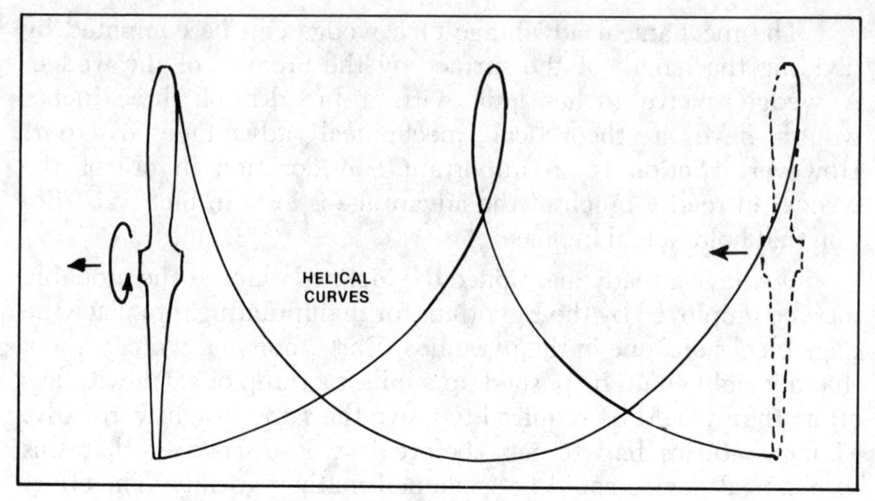

The helical motion of a propeller.

Discussion

1. When a prehistoric man or woman pried up a stone with a stick, what machine was in use? What is the principle on which the lever works?

2. Why is a seesaw an excellent example of a lever?

3. How were the rocks for Stone-henge probably moved?

4. What is a lever of the first class?

5. What is a lever of the second class?

6. What is a lever of the third class?

7. What is the law of the lever? How does the seesaw illustrate this?

8. How can the mechanical advantage of the lever be increased?

9. What kind of force must the fulcrum exert?

10. What is the difference between a wheel and a wheel and axle?

11. How was the wheel probably discovered? When was the wheel and axle combination probably first used? For what purpose?

12. What animal made possible the early use of the wheel and axle for transportation?

13. Name some other early uses of the wheel.

14. What can a crank do? What did it make possible?

15. What is the third basic machine? Describe its simplest form. What was this device used for in ancient times?

16. What is a block and tackle and what can it do?

17. What is the mechanical advantage of a simple block and tackle? How can this be increased?

18. Explain how a movable pulley acts as a lever of the second class.

19. What are the remaining basic machines that are sometimes grouped together?

20. What are wedges used for? What were some practical applications in very early times? Name some we use today.

21. How can you compute the mechanical advantage of a wedge?

22. Why is much of this mechanical advantage lost in reality? How does this relate to the nail?

23. What did ancient builders know about moving weights up hills or ramps?

24. How can you compute the mechanical advantage of an inclined plane? Why would a greater effort than this be required in practice?

25. How is the inclined plane related to the screw? Describe a helix.

26. What were some early uses of the screw?

27. What are some examples of its modern use? Why is it particularly important?

28. What kind of motion does the propeller of a ship or an airplane have? What is the result of this motion?

Review

A. Match the terms on the left with the statements on the right.

1. Lever	____A pulley contained in a housing.
2. Fulcrum	____A corkscrew-shaped figure.
3. Effort End	____A triangle of material tapering to a thin edge.
4. Load End	____The resistance to motion produced by two bodies moving in contact with each other.
5. Axle	____A machine consisting of a rigid bar that turns on a point.
6. Crank	____A helical inclined plane often used as a fastening device.
7. Pulley	____The point on which a lever turns.
8. Block	____A surface like a ramp that is set at an angle to the horizontal.
9. Block and Tackle	____The point where there is resisting force on a lever.
10. Wedge	____A device used to raise heavy weights for short distances.

11. Inclined Plane	____A bent shaft or arm for transmitting motion, changing reciprocating to rotary motion or the opposite.
12. Screw	____The point where force is applied to a lever.
13. Helix	____A shaft on which a wheel rotates.
14. Jack	____A wedge which can be used as a fastening device because of friction.
15. Friction	____A wheel with a grooved surface through which a rope, wire, or chain is passed.
16. Nail	____Combination of a fixed and a movable block.

B. Mark the effort end, the load end, and the fulcrum in each of the figures below. Indicate which class of lever each one is.

1.  1. ____________________

2. 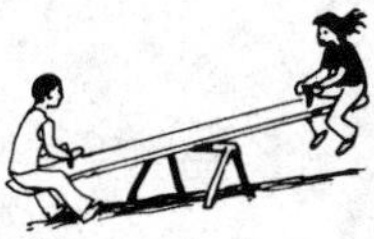 2. ____________________

3.  3. ____________________

4. 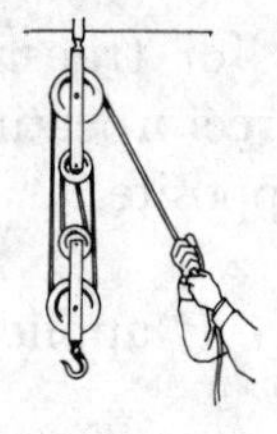 4. ____________________

5.  5. ____________________

C. What is the theoretical mechanical advantage in each of these figures? Why is the actual mechanical advantage less than the theoretical mechanical advantage?

1. 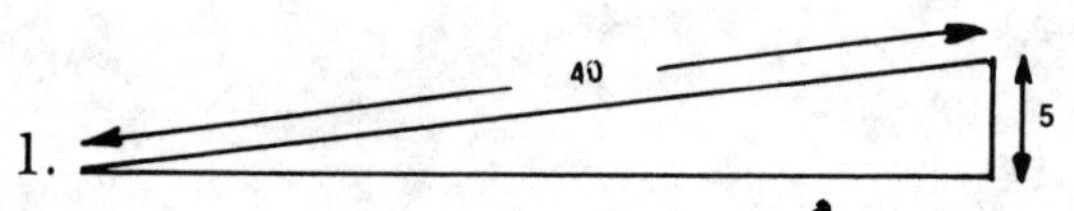

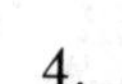
4. 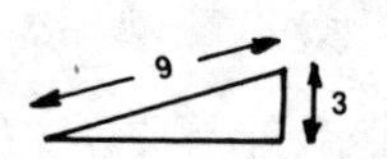

2. 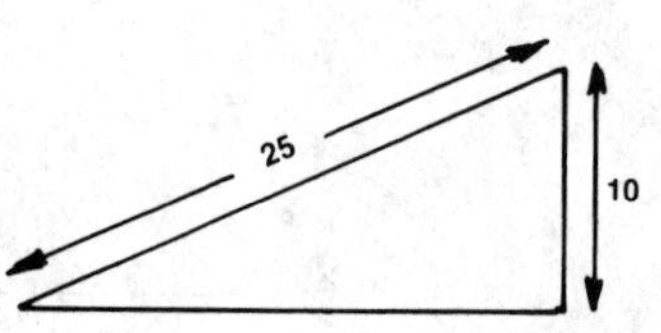

5. 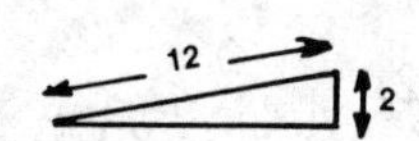

3. 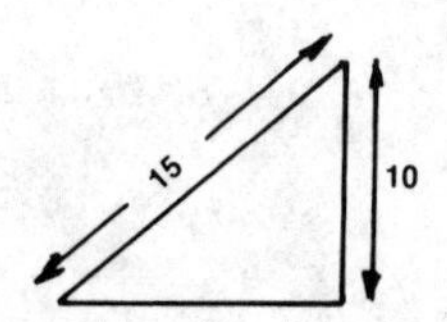

6. 16 4

UNIT FOUR
MACHINE COMPONENTS

Special Terms

Mechanism: A component of a machine that transmits or changes motion.

Kinematics: A branch of the science of mechanics that deals with aspects of motion apart from considerations of mass and force.

Gear: A wheel with teeth that can engage another wheel with teeth; gears work in pairs to transmit or change motion.

Axial Motion: Motion around an axis, the line around which a wheel rotates.

Spur Gear: A gear with straight teeth parallel to the axis.

Pinion: The smaller member of a pair of gears or the smallest gear of a series; gear is used to designate the larger member.

Helical Gear: A gear with teeth cut in the shape of a helix.

Herringbone Gear: A helical gear with two sets of teeth at equal but opposite angles to each other.

Bevel Gear: A gear with teeth slanted at an angle to the plane of the wheel itself.

Worm Gear: A mechanism consisting of a gear that meshes with a *worm*, a screw with helical teeth.

Rack and Pinion: A gear mechanism composed of a rack (a straight bar with teeth) and a pinion (a spur gear).

Cam: A rotating or sliding piece of machinery that acts as part of a pair to impart or receive motion.

Follower: The other part of a cam mechanism, usually a rod and shaft that receives and transmits motion from the cam.

Linkage: A mechanism consisting of rods connected to each other by joints that permit motion.

Spring: An elastic material that returns to its original shape after being forced out of that shape.

Leaf Spring: A spring made of strips, rather than a spiral, of elastic material which is usually metal.

Ratchet: A mechanism that works with a *pawl*. The ratchet is a bar or wheel with inclined teeth; the pawl is usually a rod that can drop between the teeth to permit motion in only one direction.

Vocabulary Practice

1. How does a *mechanism* differ from a machine?
2. What is studied in *kinematics*?
3. Describe a *gear*.
4. What is *axial motion*?
5. How are the teeth cut in a *spur gear*?
6. What is a *pinion*?
7. How are the teeth cut in a *helical gear*?
8. Describe a *herringbone gear*.
9. How are the teeth cut in a *bevel gear*?
10. What is a *worm gear*?
11. Describe a *rack and pinion* mechanism.
12. What is a *cam*?
13. What is a *follower*?
14. What is a *linkage*?

15. Describe a *spring*.

16. How does a *leaf spring* differ from the usual type of spring?

17. Discuss a *ratchet* and *pawl*.

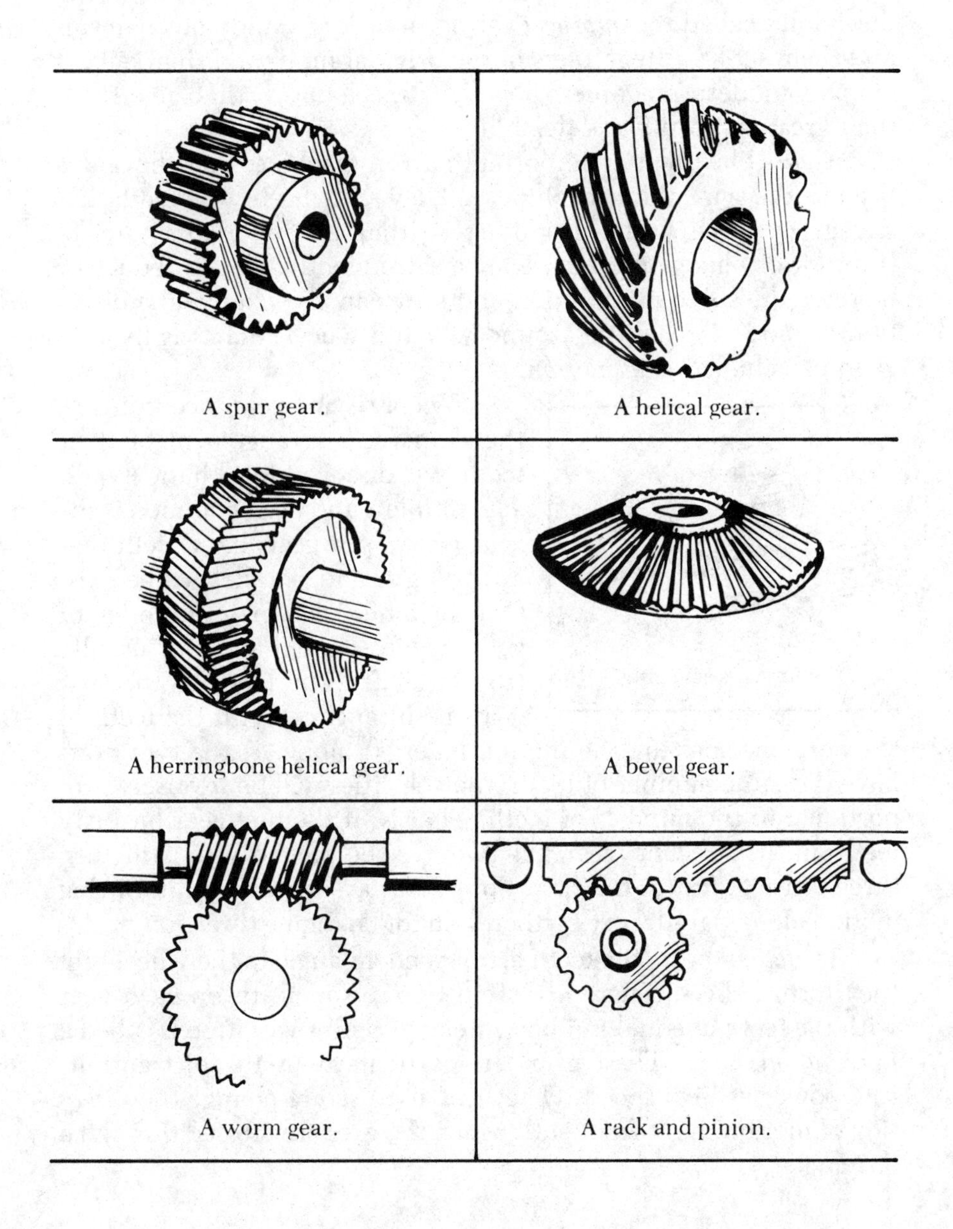

A spur gear.

A helical gear.

A herringbone helical gear.

A bevel gear.

A worm gear.

A rack and pinion.

Machine Components

Essentially all machines are variations or combinations of the six basic types described in the previous unit. There are a number of different kinds of *mechanisms* or components that transmit motion or change it in one way or another. Modern machines and their components have become so complex that a branch of the science of mechanics called *kinematics* evolved in order to study mechanisms and their actions. Regardless of the original input and final output of most modern machines, it is their mechanisms that give them their great versatility and flexibility.

Gears play such an important part in machines that they have become the symbol for machinery. They are wheels with teeth that engage or mesh with each other so that they work in pairs to transmit or change motion. They are frequently used to reduce or increase the speed of a motion and they can also change the direction of motion. The line around which a wheel rotates is its axis; gears can change *axial motion*.

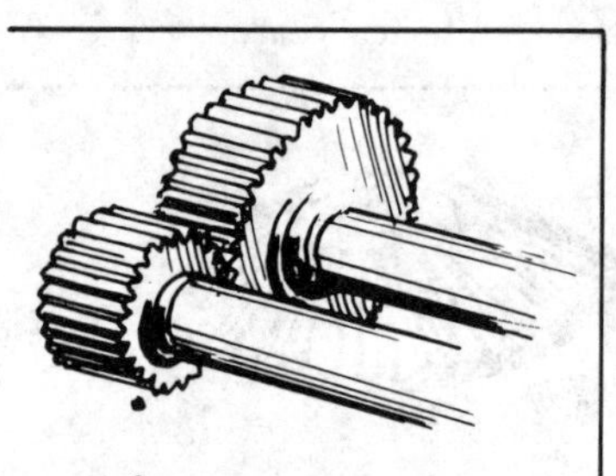

Spur gears engaging.

By classifying gears according to the shape and arrangement of their teeth we discover four basic types. The simplest and most common is the *spur gear*. Spur gears have teeth that are straight and parallel to the axis. One member of a pair or series of gears receives input motion, usually from a shaft. The teeth of the first gear mesh (engage) with the teeth of the next one, passing the motion (energy) along. If the two gears have the same number of teeth, the velocities will be inversely proportional to the number of teeth. That is, if the first gear has sixty teeth and the second gear has twenty, the second gear will turn three times as fast as the first. Spur gears are used for transmitting motion along parallel axes rather than for changing direction.

In *helical gears* the teeth are at such an angle to the wheel that they form helices. There are often two sets of teeth on each gear with the teeth at equal but opposite angles; this variation is called a *herringbone gear*. These gears are particularly useful for transmitting power at high speeds. They are also used to change the direction of motion, most frequently when the axes are crossed through a 90° angle.

A bevel is a surface that is slanted at an angle in relation to another surface. In a *bevel gear* the teeth are slanted in relation to the plane of the wheel. Bevel gears are useful in changing the direction of motion, the change being in proportion to the angle of the beveled surface. One variation is the spiral bevel gear which has the same relationship to bevel gears as helical gears have to spur gears. With a bevel gear one tooth at a time has to bear the entire load but in the spiral configuration more than one tooth always remains in contact.

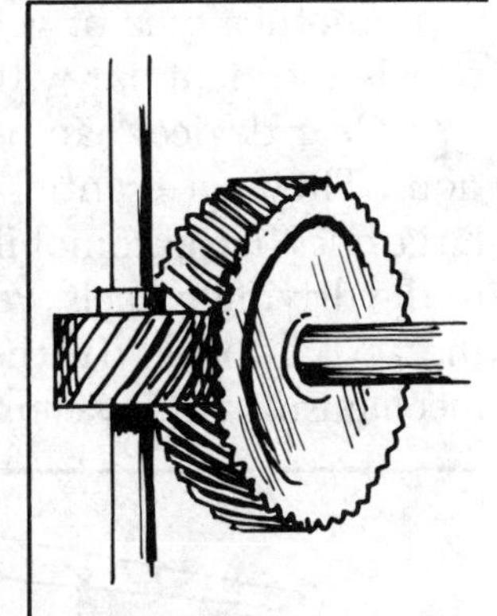
Helical gears engaging.

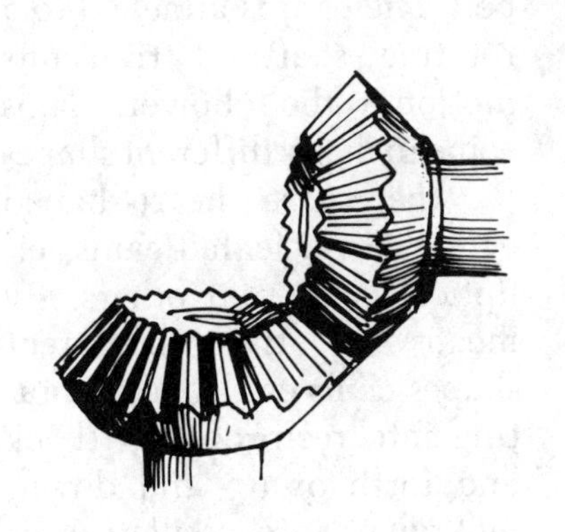
Spiral bevel gears engaging.

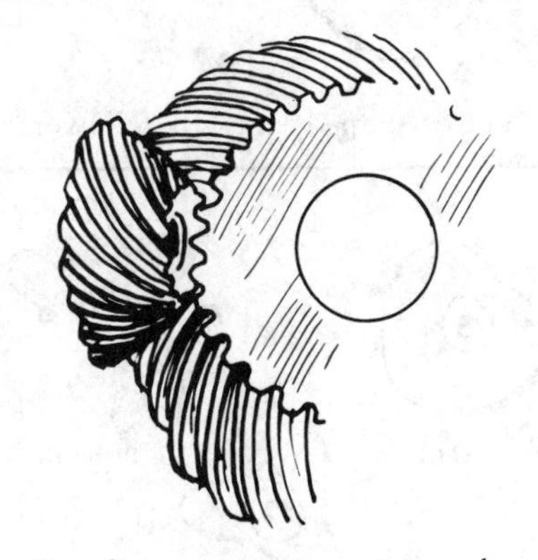
Bevel gears engaging at an angle.

The fourth basic type is called the *worm gear*. Basically a pair consists of the gear itself, a wheel with teeth which meshes with a worm—a screw which is a helix wrapped around a cylinder. A variation is a worm shaped in an hour-glass figure. Worm gears are used primarily for changing the direction of axial motion.

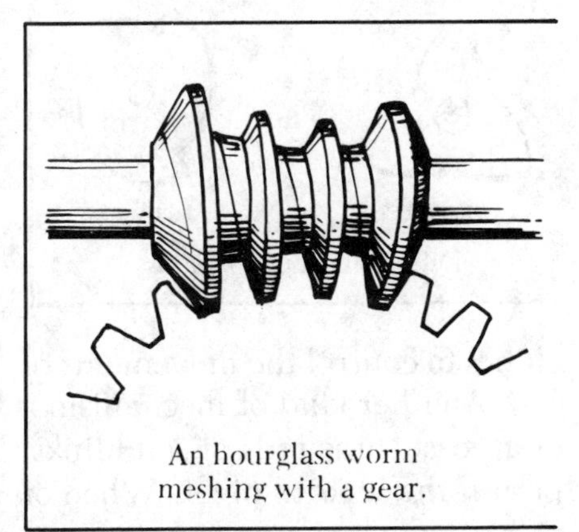
An hourglass worm meshing with a gear.

Another type of gear mechanism is the *rack and pinion*. The rack is a straight bar with teeth and the pinion is a small spur gear.

Gear devices can be used in a variety of shapes and combinations. They are essential elements in tiny devices like watches and in large ones like automobiles. Without the gears that transmit motion to the driving wheels we could not have the kind of transportation that exists today. In their variations on the basic machines gear mechanisms are key elements that produce enormous versatility.

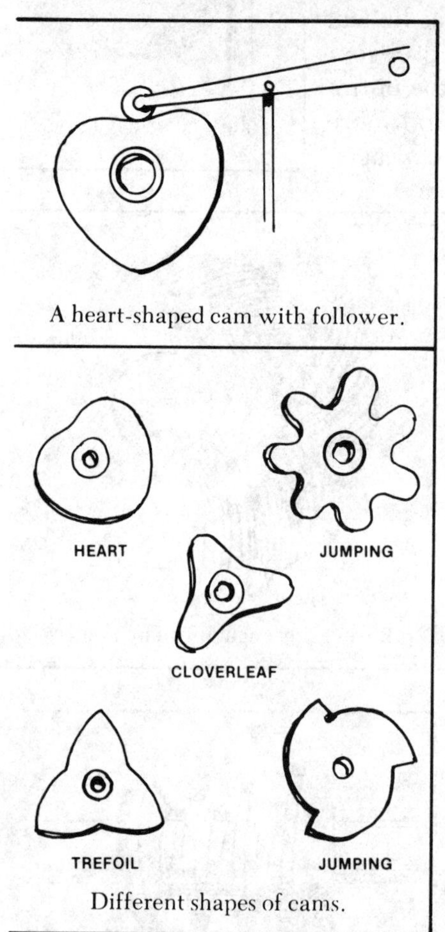

A heart-shaped cam with follower.

Different shapes of cams.

Another kind of mechanism is the *cam*. Like the gear, it consists of a pair of components; the cam itself is the input member and the *follower* is the output member. The cam is attached to a rotating shaft; it transmits motion to the follower. Cams come in many different shapes — there are heart-shaped cams, clover-leafed cams, elliptical cams and others. By means of these different shapes cams can change rotating into reciprocating (back and forth or up and down) motion or into oscillating or vibrating motion. The follower is usually a rod or shaft.

Cams can transmit exact motions at specific times in a cycle. They are therefore useful where the timing of complex motions is important. They are in automobile engines to raise and lower the valves and in sewing machines to control the movements of the needle.

Another kind of mechanism is known as a *linkage*; it is a series of at least three rods or solid links that are connected by joints that permit the links to pivot. When one link is fixed the other links can move only in paths that are predetermined. Like cams, linkages are used to change the direction of motion, to transmit different kinds of motion, or to provide variations in timing in different parts of a cycle by varying the lengths of the links in relation to each other.

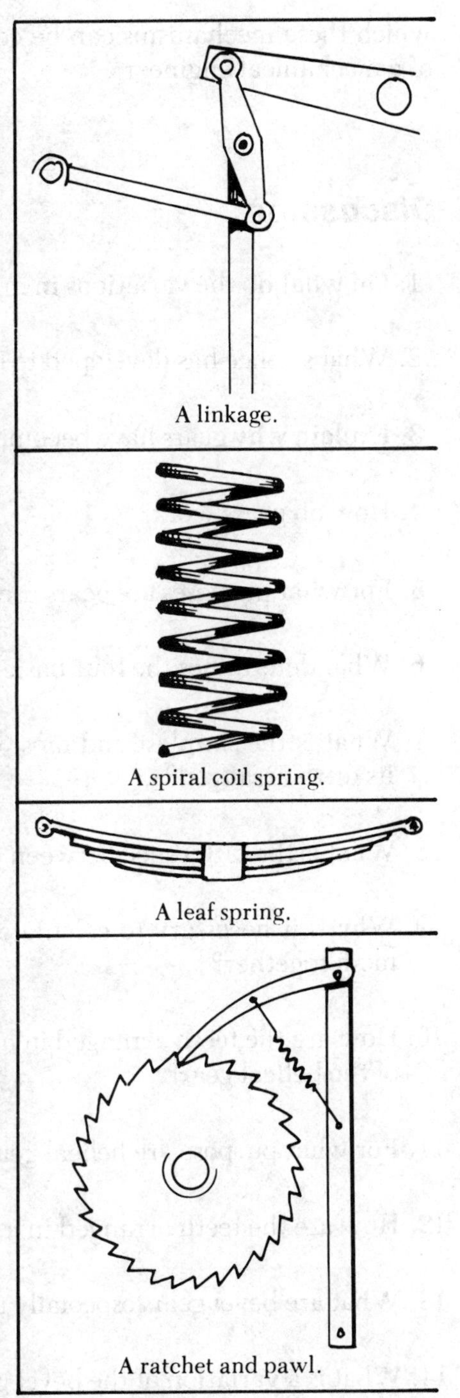
A linkage.

A spiral coil spring.

A leaf spring.

A ratchet and pawl.

The *spring* is a mechanism that is used in a wide variety of machines; it is frequently an elastic helical coil that returns to its original shape after being distorted. Springs are essential components in watches; in some cam mechanisms they hold the follower in place; they are found in scales and they help to cushion an automobile ride. There are many variations on the basic coiled or spiral spring, including the *leaf spring* which is made of strips of elastic material and springs that depend on the compression and expansion of air.

A *ratchet* is another paired mechanism consisting of a wheel with teeth and a pawl which drops into the spaces between the teeth. The ratchet mechanism is used to prevent a motion from being reversed or to change reciprocating into rotary motion.

This is a brief introduction to the complex world of machine components. The infinite number of combinations and variations in which these mechanisms can be combined is the heart of the work of a mechanical engineer.

Discussion

1. On what do the variations in machines depend?
2. What science has developed to study mechanisms?
3. Explain why gears have become the symbol for machinery.
4. How do gears work?
5. For what purposes are gears used?
6. What determines the four basic types of gears?
7. What is the simplest and most common kind of gear? How are its teeth arranged?
8. What is the difference between the gear and the pinion?
9. Why is it necessary to calculate the ratio of teeth in gears that mesh together?
10. How are the teeth arranged in helical gears? What is a variation of the helical gear?
11. For what purpose are helical gears particularly useful?
12. How are the teeth arranged in a bevel gear?
13. What are bevel gears especially useful for?
14. What is a variation of the bevel gear? Discuss its advantage.

15. Describe the worm gear and its uses.

16. What is the name for a gear mechanism with a straight bar and a small spur gear used as a pair?

17. What are some of the uses of gears? Give examples in addition to those in the reading.

18. In a cam mechanism, which is the input member and which is the output member?

19. Are all cams the same shape?

20. What are some of the things that cams do?

21. Name some machines which use cams.

22. What is a linkage and how does it work?

23. How are linkages like cams?

24. What is an everyday example of a linkage? Can you think of another one?

25. Discuss the spring mechanism.

26. What are some of its common uses? Give examples in addition to those in the reading.

27. Name some different types of springs.

28. How does a ratchet and pawl mechanism work?

29. Mechanisms are the heart of the work of a mechanical engineer. Discuss this statement.

Review

A. Match the terms on the left with the statements on the right.

1. Mechanism	____A spring made of strips rather than a spiral coil.
2. Kinematics	____A mechanism consisting of rods connected to each other by joints that permit motion.
3. Gear	____A device of elastic material, usually metal, that returns to its original shape after being distorted.
4. Axial Motion	____A branch of the science of mechanics that deals with aspects of motion apart from mass and force.
5. Pinion	____A gear with teeth slanted at an angle to the plane of the wheel itself.
6. Spur Gear	____A component of a machine that transmits or changes motion.
7. Helical Gear	____The part of a cam mechanism, usually a rod or shaft, that is the output member of the pair.
8. Bevel Gear	____Motion in the line around which a wheel rotates.
9. Worm Gear	____A piece of metal that rotates or slides to transmit or change motion.
10. Rack and Pinion	____A wheel with teeth cut at an angle to its axis; paired with a pawl it governs or prevents motion.
11. Cam	____The smaller member of a pair of gears.

12. Follower ____A wheel with teeth that can engage or mesh with another wheel with teeth.

13. Linkage ____A gear with teeth straight and parallel to the axis.

14. Spring ____A gear that meshes with a screw-like cylinder that has teeth cut in helices.

15. Leaf Spring ____A gear with teeth cut in the shape of a helix.

16. Ratchet ____A gear mechanism in which a spur gear (pinion) meshes with teeth in a straight bar (rack).

B. Identify each of the mechanisms below. Try to label each part.

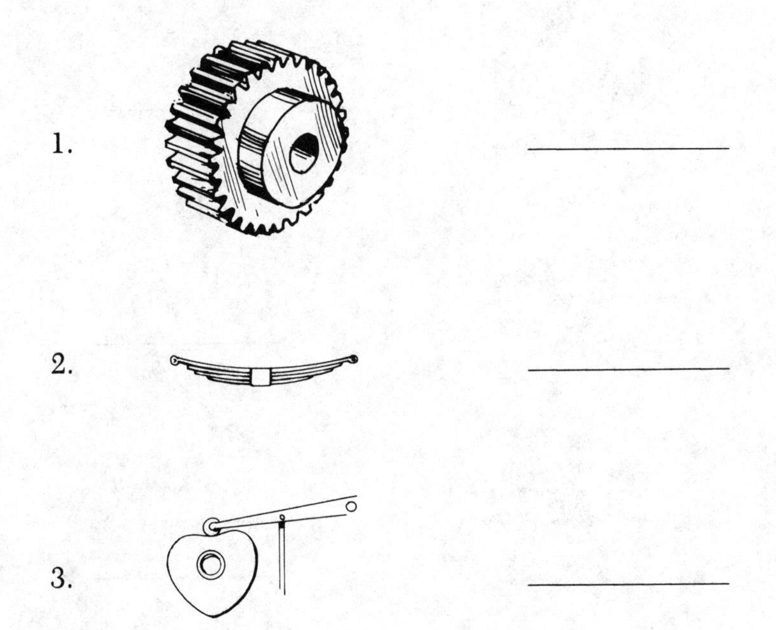

4.  ______________

5. 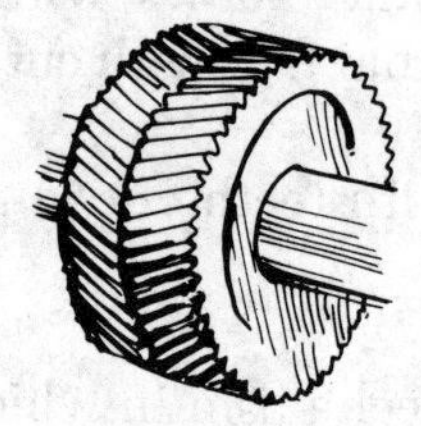 ______________

6. 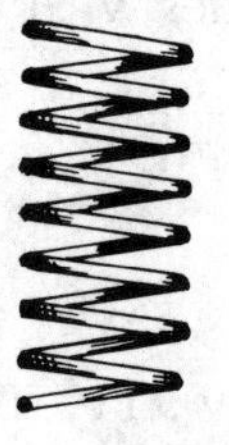 ______________

7. 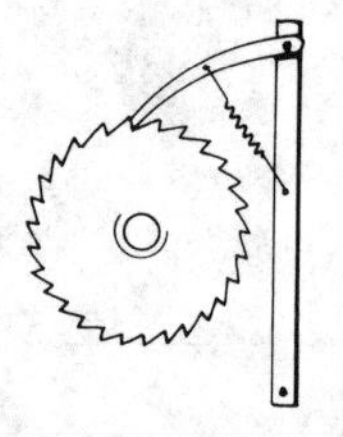 ______________

8. 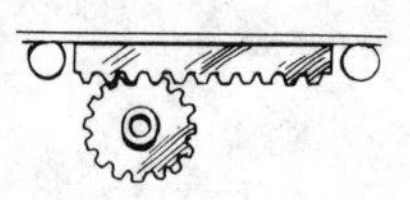 ______________

9. 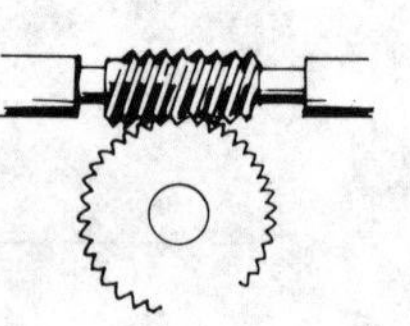 ______________

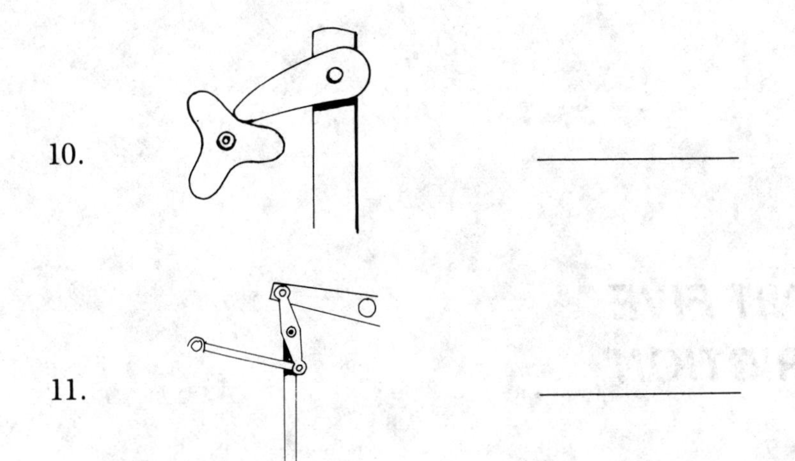
10.
11.

UNIT FIVE
FRICTION

Special Terms

Friction: The resistance to relative motion of two bodies moving in contact with each other.

Coefficient of Friction: The constant ratio of the friction to the force pressing the surfaces together.

Static Friction: The resistance to motion between two bodies in contact with each other but at rest.

Sliding Friction: The resistance to continued motion when one body has started to move.

Rolling Friction: The resistance to motion when one or more bodies is rotating or rolling, but not on the same axis.

Babbitt Metal: An alloy or mixture of tin, copper, and antimony with a low coefficient of friction.

Teflon: A plastic containing fluorine with a low coefficient of friction.

Antimony: A metalloid element, silvery-white, brittle yet soft with the unusual quality of expanding when solidified; used as a constituent of alloys.

Lubrication: Application of a substance, usually oil or grease (a *lubricant*) to reduce friction.

Polymers: Long, heavy, complex molecules forming repeating structural units that occur in many plastics.

Bearing: That part of a machine which supports parts in relative motion.

Ball Bearings: Bearings containing small round balls, sometimes known as *anti-friction bearings.*

Cage: A device to hold and separate bearings.

Races: Rings within which cages of bearings are sealed.

Roller Bearings: Bearings with rolling elements in the shape of cylinders or *tapered* cylinders or *needles;* they have a greater load-carrying capacity but more friction than ball bearings of similar size.

Non-contact Bearings: Bearings that touch only at rest; in motion they are separated by gas or fluid.

Brakes and Braking Devices: Devices to slow and control motion in a machine, usually through some form of friction.

Drum Brake: A braking device with friction material pressing on the inside of a metal drum.

Fading: Lowering the coefficient of friction in a braking device.

Disk Brake: A braking device of metal disks which can be brought into contact against friction pads.

Clutch: A device by which different parts of a machine can be connected or disconnected without bringing the parts to rest.

Disk Clutch: A clutching device that uses disks lined with friction material and no lubrication.

Vocabulary Practice

1. Describe *friction.*
2. What is the *coefficient of friction*?
3. How do *static, sliding,* and *rolling friction* differ from each other?
4. What is *babbitt metal*?
5. What is *teflon*?
6. What is *antimony* used for?
7. What does *lubrication* mean? What is a *lubricant*?

8. What are *polymers*?

9. What is a *bearing*?

10. What are *ball bearings*?

11. What do *cage* and *races* mean in connection with bearings?

12. What are some different types of *roller bearings*?

13. Describe *non-contact bearings.*

14. What are *brakes* or *braking devices*?

15. Describe a *drum brake* and a *disk brake.*

16. What does *fading* do to braking devices?

17. What does a *clutch* do?

18. How does a *disk clutch* work?

Friction

Friction reduces the efficiency of machines but it is also indispensable. When you try to walk on ice, slipping and sliding and perhaps falling down, you realize the importance of friction. Ice has a low *coefficient of friction* and that is what makes it so difficult to walk on. Without friction it would be impossible to walk at all and our trains and cars could not move.

There are three different kinds of mechanical friction: *static, sliding,* and *rolling.* Static friction is the resistance to motion between two bodies in contact but at rest. The resistance of static friction is greater than that of sliding friction which is resistance to continued motion after one body has started to move. Rolling friction occurs when resistance is reduced to its lowest degree by rotary motion not on the same axis.

Ice has a low coefficient of friction.

Note these three kinds of friction at work: it takes a stronger effort to put a box into motion (static friction) then it does to keep it moving across the floor once started (sliding friction); if there are rollers under the box it takes still less effort to keep it in motion (rolling friction).

One way to reduce friction in machines is through the materials for the parts that contact each other. The *coefficient of friction* is the constant ratio of the friction to the force pressing the surfaces together. Coefficients have been equated for different common materials using the three types of friction. Steel on steel or glass on glass have high coefficients but some new substances have much lower coefficients. One of these is *babbitt metal*, an alloy made of tin, copper, and *antimony*; another is *teflon*, a plastic containing fluorine that is sometimes used in cooking utensils.

Another way of reducing friction is by means of *lubrication*, applying oil or grease to the points or surfaces where the parts of a machine contact each other. Petroleum products are the principal modern lubricants; some of them include *polymers*, the long, heavy, complex molecules that occur in plastics.

A vital mechanism for reducing friction is the *bearing* which basically is a device that bears the friction of parts in motion. Often one of the parts will be moving and the other will be stationary. Logs used to move heavy stones in early times were the primitive

Lubricating a car.

form of a bearing. They were efficient because they changed sliding friction to rolling friction, thereby decreasing the effort necessary to move the stones.

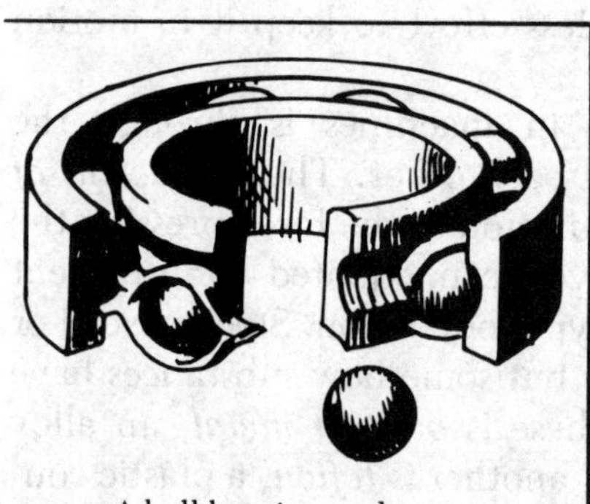
A ball bearing and cage.

Reducing friction between the parts of a machine is the principal purpose of bearings. Different types have been designed for use at various points of contact to fit the kinds of motion at work. Probably the most familiar are *ball bearings* which are used in many machines. Small balls are fitted into a *cage*, a container that separates them. Cage and bearings are then sealed, often in a lubricant, between rings which are called *races*. The entire assembly is a ball bearing.

Another familiar type is the *roller bearing*, a modern version of the logs that were used as primitive bearings. Roller bearings contain small cylinders on which the bearing races can roll. They are usually fitted with the same kind of holding cage and races as ball bearings. In order to sustain pressure from different directions, bearing rollers are sometimes *tapered* or shaped like cut-off cones

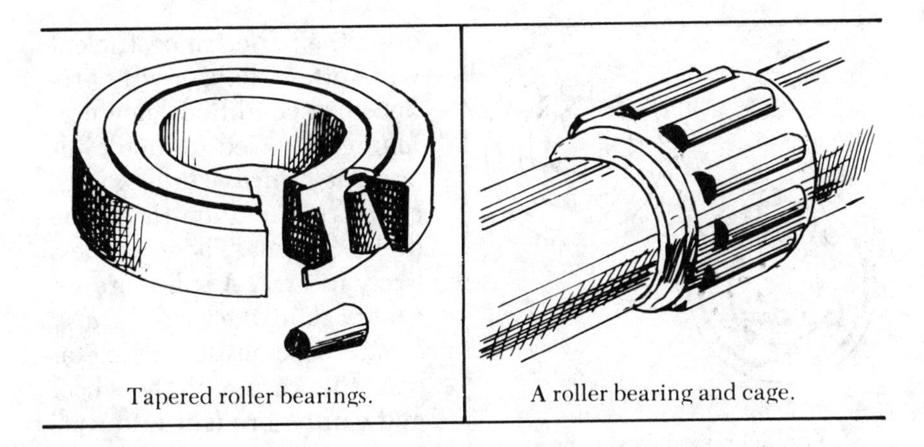

Tapered roller bearings. A roller bearing and cage.

and set at an angle to the races. A variation is the *needle bearing* with cylinders of very small diameter. Needle bearings need not be contained in a cage or between races. Their advantage is greater load-carrying capacity with more friction than ball bearings of comparable size.

A modern development is the *non-contact bearing* in which there is contact between the machine parts only at rest; when in motion they are separated by a thin layer of gas or fluid. This prevents wear between the moving parts. Non-contact bearings have been developed for such complex and sophisticated systems as missile guidance. The possibility of using cushions of compressed air in transportation systems has been discussed frequently in recent years.

While bearings are used to minimize friction other mechanical devices put friction to work. The car that rolls without acceleration is gradually brought to a stop by friction. A long gradual stop is far from suitable, however, to traffic conditions where speed must be controlled and where sudden and frequent stops are necessary. *Braking devices* put friction to work to provide the necessary control over motion in automobiles and other kinds of machines.

The most common types of brakes ordinarily consist of a rotating component that is brought into contact with a friction component designed so that the mechanical energy is changed into heat which is dissipated into the air. The friction material may be metal, ceramic, or a substance like asbestos. Old-fashioned automobile brakes were made of a steel band that could be pressed down against the outside of the brake drum. When they got wet, how-

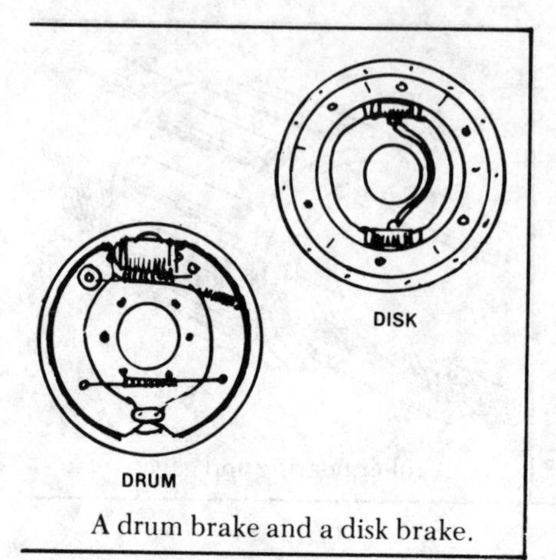

A drum brake and a disk brake.

ever, their friction coefficient was often dangerously reduced, a condition known as *fading*. This led to the development of *drum brakes* with a friction lining on the inside of the drum. These are less likely to fade. A still more recent braking device is the *disk brake*. It consists of metal disks that turn with the wheel and can be brought into contact against friction pads.

Another mechanism necessary for road vehicles is a *clutch* device so that the motor shaft can be connected or disconnected from the wheel shaft while the motor is running. The type in common use today is the *disk clutch* in which connection is made by applying pressure so that pairs of disks lined with friction material are brought into contact or released to increase or decrease power to the output shaft. In many cars pressure comes when the driver steps on the clutch pedal; with some automatic transmissions pressure is applied automatically through fluids as speed changes. Any kind of clutch depends on friction.

Discussion

1. What does friction do to the efficiency of machines?

2. What does friction make possible?

3. Name the three different kinds of friction.

4. Which kind of friction offers the greatest resistance? The least? Explain and give an example.

5. How can the choice of materials in a machine help reduce friction?

6. What are some substances that have low coefficients of friction?
7. What is another way of reducing friction?
8. Name the principal lubricants and some new variations.
9. Discuss a common mechanism used to reduce friction.
10. Why are logs efficient when used to move heavy objects?
11. What is the most familiar type of bearing? How is it usually enclosed in a machine?
12. What is the modern version of the logs that were used as primitive bearings?
13. Why are roller bearings sometimes tapered?
14. How do needle bearings differ from other types?
15. What kind of bearings have been developed for use in complex and sophisticated systems such as missile guidance?
16. Why isn't a long gradual stop suitable for automobiles?
17. How do braking devices put friction to work?
18. What do brakes ordinarily consist of? What are some friction materials used in brakes?
19. How did old-fashioned automobile brakes work? What was wrong with them?
20. Describe more recent developments in automobile brakes.
21. What is the purpose of a clutch device in an automobile?
22. What type of clutch is in common use today? How does it use friction to do its work?

Review

A. Match the terms on the left with the statements on the right.

1. Friction	____A plastic that contains flourine with a low coefficient of friction.
2. Coefficient of Friction	____Long, heavy, complex molecules that occur in many plastics.
3. Static Friction	____Devices to slow and control motion in machines.
4. Sliding Friction	____Bearings separated by gas or fluid when a machine is in motion.
5. Rolling Friction	____A device to hold balls or rollers in order to keep them separate.
6. Babbitt Metal	____Application of a substance such as grease or oil to reduce friction.
7. Teflon	____Bearings containing cylinders.
8. Antimony	____The resistance to motion produced by two bodies moving in contact with each other.
9. Lubrication	____Devices to connect or disconnect parts of a machine when it is in motion.
10. Polymers	____The constant ratio of friction to the force pressing the surfaces together.
11. Bearing	____The resistance to motion when one or both bodies is rotating on different axes.
12. Cage	____Bearings with parts in the shape of cut-off cones.

13. Races ____The resistance to motion between two bodies in contact but at rest.

14. Ball Bearings ____An alloy of tin, copper, and antimony with a low coefficient of friction.

15. Roller Bearings ____The resistance to continued motion when one body has started to move.

16. Tapered Bearings ____A brittle yet soft metalloid element which expands when solidified; used in alloys.

17. Needle Bearings ____Rings within which cages containing bearings are sealed.

18. Non-contact Bearings ____Bearings containing cylinders of very small diameter.

19. Braking Devices ____Part of a machine which bears the friction of parts in relative motion.

20. Clutching Devices ____Bearings containing small round balls.

B. Summarize the methods and devices used to minimize or reduce friction in machines. Include others not mentioned in the reading.

____

____

____

C. Discuss mechanical devices that take advantage of friction. Include some that are not mentioned in the reading.

UNIT SIX
STEAM ENGINES

Special Terms

Steam: The invisible vapor into which water is changed when it is heated to the boiling point.

Boiler: A vessel in which water is boiled to produce steam.

Condense: To return to a liquid state, as when steam reverts to water. The process is *condensation* and a device that causes the process to take place is a *condenser*.

Vacuum: A space devoid of matter. Vacuums are *partial*, not complete.

Valve: A device that opens or closes to control the flow of liquids or gases.

Piston: A rod or disk that can move up or down within a hollow cylinder.

Walking Beam: A lever that works on the seesaw principle, with input on one side and output on the other side of the fulcrum.

Crankshaft: A shaft driving or driven by a crank.

Sun-and-Planet Gears: An arrangement in which a smaller gear (the planet) rotates around a larger gear (the sun).

Safety Valve: A valve that opens automatically when steam or other pressure exceeds a predetermined amount.

Internal Combustion Engine: A heat engine in which combustion (burning of fuel) takes place within a cylinder, as in engines that burn gasoline. Steam engines are not internal combustion engines.

Turbine: A rotating machine with blades set and kept in motion by water, steam, or gas.

Generator: A machine that produces energy by rotating through a magnetic field; the shaft of the generator is often turned by a turbine.

Vocabulary Practice

1. What is *steam* and how is it produced?
2. What is the purpose of a *boiler*?
3. What does *condense* mean? What is the process called, and what is the device used for the process?
4. What is a *vacuum*?
5. Describe a *valve*.
6. Describe a *piston*.
7. Describe a *walking beam*.
8. What does a *crankshaft* do?
9. What is the arrangement of *sun-and-planet gears*?
10. What does a *safety valve* do?
11. What powers an *internal combustion engine*? Are steam engines internal combustion devices?
12. Describe a *turbine*.
13. What is a *generator*? What is the relation of the turbine to the generator?

Steam Engines

Steam was used to provide power for a kind of mechanical toy in ancient times by an ingenious Greek inventor named Hero of Alexandria. But it was not until the end of the seventeenth century that steam was harnessed for machines that could perform work. The development of these machines is usually regarded as the beginning of the Industrial Revolution. The first steam engines were designed for the practical purpose of pumping water out of mines; the first one to be sold commercially was called the Miner's Friend.

When water is boiled it creates a volume of steam greater than the original amount of water. This greater volume can burst a *boiler* unless it is released. When the vessel is cooled the steam *condenses* rapidly so that it returns to its liquid state. The result is a *partial vacuum* in the vessel that contained the steam. It was this vacuum that was put to work by Thomas Savery and later Thomas Newcomen in the earliest practical steam engines.

In the Savery engine steam from a boiler entered a container. When the container was filled cold water was poured over it thereby creating a partial vacuum that sucked water up into the container. When the container was refilled with steam the water was forced up to a higher level. The *valves* that controlled the admission of steam to the container as well as the cold water to cause condensation had to be worked by hand on this engine.

The Newcomen engine was an important advance over the Savery engine. The *piston* was attached by a chain to a *walking beam*, a heavy lever that worked on the seesaw principle. The other end of the walking beam was attached to a shaft that worked a pump deep in a mine. When the piston was at the top of the steam-filled cylinder, water was shot into the cylinder condensing the steam. Atmospheric pressure forced the piston down, simultaneously raising water from the mine. Steam was allowed to fill the cylinder and the piston moved up to the top, ready for another stroke.

After the Newcomen engine had been in service for a time, it was discovered that the valves that controlled the steam and cold water could be automated—that is, they could be attached to the walking beam in such a way as to turn them on or off by the action of the beam at certain points during the cycle.

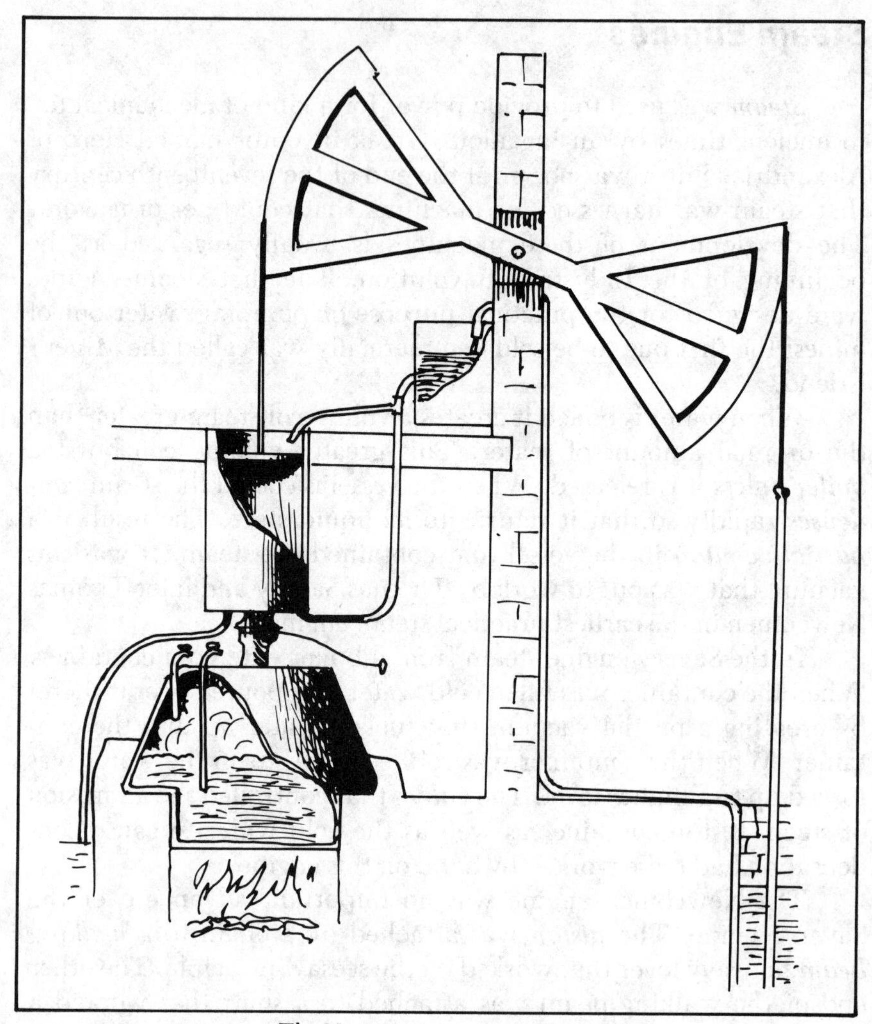

The Newcomen steam engine.

The next important figure in the development of the steam engine was James Watt. He is often credited with being the inventor of the steam engine but what he did in fact was improve on the preceding machines. Watt's contributions were of enormous importance in the history of machines and mechanical engineering. One great disadvantage of the Newcomen engine was the amount of fuel it used because so much heat was lost through the alternate heating and cooling of the cylinder. Watt's solution was to separate the cylinder and the condenser so that the cylinder could be kept hot and the condenser cool at the same time. Watt's engine was a great success since it used only one-third as much fuel as the Newcomen engine.

James Pickard, who had been employed by Watt, took the next big step in the development of the steam engine. This was to change the reciprocating motion of the piston to rotary motion that could turn wheels. Pickard attached the piston to a connecting rod that turned a *crankshaft* to produce rotary motion.

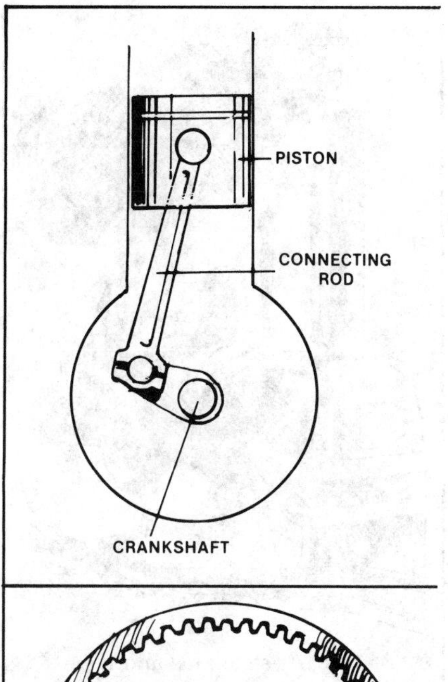

Pickard took out a patent on his crankshaft design so Watt had to evolve other devices to produce rotary motion. One of his ideas was the arrangement called *sun-and-planet gears.* A smaller gear (the planet) rotates around the outer face of a larger gear (the sun).

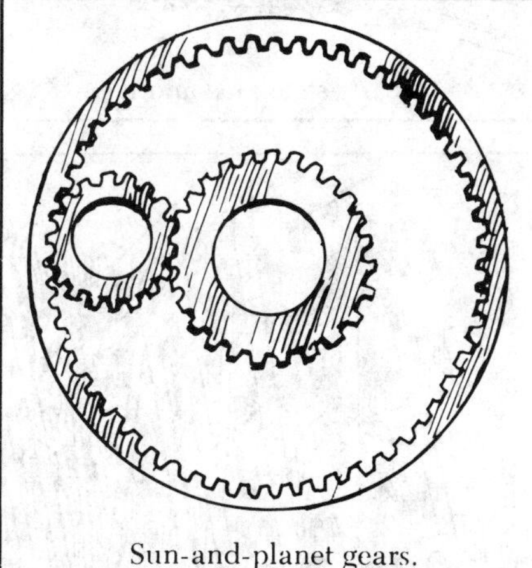
Sun-and-planet gears.

In these early days of steam engines the technical accomplishments we take for granted were difficult to achieve. Machining of parts was not exact and it was impossible to build boilers that could withstand steam at high pressure. In Watt's day it was the vacuum created by condensing steam that actually performed work. As boilermaking improved it was possible to superheat the water and thus increase the steam pressure. This, in combination with *safety valves*, made steam engines far more efficient by putting the pressure to work.

The nineteenth century was the age of steam. The machines of Savery, Newcomen, Watt, and their successors were used not only for pumping water out of mines but for an increasing number of in-

An early steam locomotive.

dustrial advances. Many early applications were in the manufacture of textiles but inventors were soon at work on the problem of using steam engines for transportation. By the middle of the century trains with steampowered locomotives were becoming the world's most important form of transportation and steamships had become common on inland waterways. Before the end of the century the difficulties of building transoceanic steamships had been solved. Thousands of factories manufacturing hundreds of products used steam power. A

A 19th century belt-driven factory.

familiar sight at the end of the century was the factory or workroom with a whole network of belts that provided drives for other devices such as lathes, drill presses, and sewing machines. These belts were a cause of frequent industrial accidents.

By the end of the century the preeminence of steam power was being threatened by two new power sources: electricity and internal combustion. Electric motors come within the field of electrical engineering and will not be discussed at any length in this book. It should be pointed out, however, that they provided greater safety in industrial operations since the shafts and belts used with steam engines were replaced by wires inside walls or under floors. The *internal combustion engine* will be examined in the following unit.

The twentieth century has seen the displacement of steam from many of its former uses in transportation and industry. We now take for granted the fact that cars are powered by internal combustion engines that burn gasoline. In the early days of the automobile there was experimentation with steam cars; some steam automobiles were even marketed successfully for a number of years. With the world's supply of petroleum now in question there is some renewed interest in steam as one alternate source of energy.

Steam still plays one vital role today in generating electricity. In an electric power plant a *turbine* drives the shaft of a *generator* which creates electricity by turning through a magnetic field. In a relatively small proportion of electric plants the turbine is activated by water power; in the majority it is steam that drives the turbine. A blast of steam strikes the blades of the turbine to make them revolve at a high rate of speed.

Even in electric generating plants that use nuclear energy it is steam that actually moves the turbines. The heat released by nuclear fission—the breaking apart of the particles in the center of an atom—is used to boil water. When the water is converted to steam at high pressure it drives the blades of a turbine, just as in a conventional power plant.

Discussion

1. When was steam first used to perform work?

2. Discuss the historical significance of the development of steam engines.

3. What was the first steam engine designed to do?

4. What happens to water when it is boiled?

5. What happens when the vessel in which water has been boiled is cooled? What is the result of this cooling?

6. How did the Savery engine work? How were the valves operated?

7. How did the Newcomen engine improve on the Savery engine?

8. What part did the walking beam play in the Newcomen engine?

9. How were the valves on the Newcomen engine "automated"?

10. What is Watt often credited with? What did he do in fact? Why was it such a great success?

11. Describe Watt's improvement on Newcomen's engine.

12. What step did Pickard take in the development of the steam engine?

13. How did this affect Watt?

14. What device did Watt invent to change reciprocating to rotary motion?

15. Discuss some of the difficulties of early boiler-making.

16. What developments made it possible to utilize steam pressure?

17. What made the nineteenth century the age of steam?

18. Describe a nineteenth century factory.

19. Name two new power sources that threatened the preeminence of steam by the end of the nineteenth century. What was one major advantage of electricity?

20. Have automobiles always used internal combustion engines? Why is there renewed interest in the possibility of other kinds of engines for cars?

21. In what area does steam still play a vital part?

22. Explain how turbines and generators help to produce electriity. What powers the turbines?

23. How is steam used in electric generating plants that utilize nuclear energy?

Review

A. Complete the following sentences with the appropriate word or phrase.

1. When water becomes a gas or vapor it is known as ________________.

2. Water can be changed into a gas or vapor by ________________ it.

3. When steam is cooled in a ________________ it quickly changes back into water.

4. Steam has a greater volume than water so when it reverts to water a ________________ is created.

5. The flow of steam and water in a steam engine is controlled by a series of ________________.

6. A rod with a disk that moves up and down inside a hollow cylinder is known as a ________________.

7. A ________________ is a lever that moves on a seesaw principle.

8. A crankshaft is connected to a ________________ in order to ________________.

9. ________________ gears are an arrangement in which a small gear revolves around a larger gear while both are circled by a third gear.

10. A ________________ opens automatically when steam or other pressure becomes too high.

11. A ________________ powered by water or steam turns a generator that produces electricity.

B. Write a short summary of the rise and decline of the steam engine. Explain why steam engines have been important to mankind even beyond the enormous amount of work they have performed. Describe the major use of steam engines today as well as their potential for use in the future.

____

____

____

____

____

____

____

UNIT SEVEN
THE INTERNAL COMBUSTION ENGINE

Special Terms

Four-stroke Engine: A device in which the piston makes four strokes or movements, two up and two down, for each charge of fuel.

Carburetor: A device in which gasoline is changed into a vapor and mixed with air.

Spark Plug: An apparatus that forms a spark causing the gas and air mixture in an internal combustion engine to burn.

Flywheel: A heavy wheel attached to the crankshaft that stores energy to help the piston make the first, second, and fourth strokes in a four- stroke cycle.

Camshaft: A device to control the valves that let gases in and out of the cylinder.

Ignition System: The devices that ignite, or set on fire, the fuel in an internal combustion engine.

Glider: An aircraft that flies without power, using air currents and gravity.

Radial Engine: An internal combustion engine used for aircraft; the cylinders are set around a center point like the radii of a circle.

Diesel Engine: An internal combustion engine that compresses air until it becomes so hot that burning occurs when fuel is injected into the cylinder; no ignition spark is needed.

Vocabulary Practice

1. Describe a *four-stroke engine.*
2. What does a *carburetor* do?
3. What does a *spark plug* do?
4. What is the purpose of a *flywheel*?
5. What does a *camshaft* do?
6. What is an *ignition system*?
7. How does a *glider* differ from a conventional airplane?
8. What is a *radial engine*?
9. Describe a *diesel engine.*

The Internal Combustion Engine

Combustion is a word for fire or burning; an internal combustion engine is one in which a fire inside the engine itself makes the engine work. Despite its polluting emissions, this is one of the most significant inventions of all time, especially because of its primary uses as a portable power source. The steam engine uses a fire in a boiler rather than inside the engine; for this reason steam engines are sometimes called external combustion engines.

Experiments with internal combustion go back to the seventeenth century. The first fuel tried was gunpowder, with a predictably explosive result. Other experiments were made with different kinds of gases including hydrogen which is explosively combustible. It was not until the second half of the nineteenth century that the development of petroleum products made possible today's internal combustion engine. Kerosene for lamps and stoves was the product first sought from petroleum while gasoline seemed nothing more than a dangerous by-product. But after other fuels had been tried it

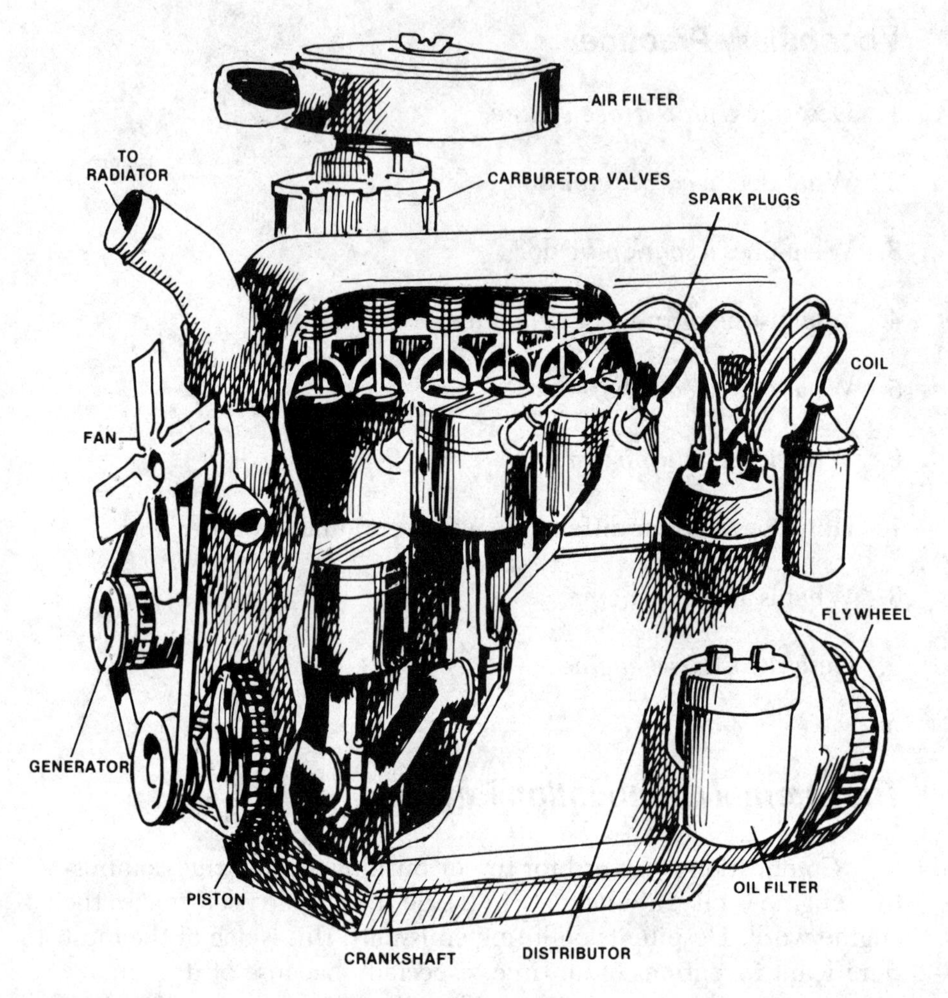

An internal combustion engine.

was gasoline that emerged as the most practical for internal combustion.

The first genuinely marketable internal combustion engine was the work of a German inventor, Nikolaus August Otto. The Otto device was a *four-stroke engine* in which each piston made four movements (two up and two down) for each combustion in the cylinder using gasoline vaporized and mixed with air in a *carburetor.* It utilized a cycle in which the combustible mixture is drawn into the cylinder of an internal combustion engine on a suction stroke (1), is compressed and ignited by a *spark plug* on a compression stroke (2), burns and performs work on an expansion stroke (3), expels combustion products on an exhaust stroke (4).

Since only the third stroke produces work, the piston needs help over the other strokes. This is given by a *flywheel* attached to the crankshaft. The flywheel in effect stores energy from the power stroke; this energy then carries the piston through the three strokes until the next power stroke caused by the combustion is repeated.

Another necessary component of the four-stroke engine is a *camshaft* which controls the cams that open or close valves to let gases in and out of the cylinder. The camshaft makes one revolution for every two of the crankshaft since the valves open only on every other stroke.

The engine designed by Otto was an immediate success. When he died in 1891, 30,000 of his engines had been sold, but they were suitable only for sta-

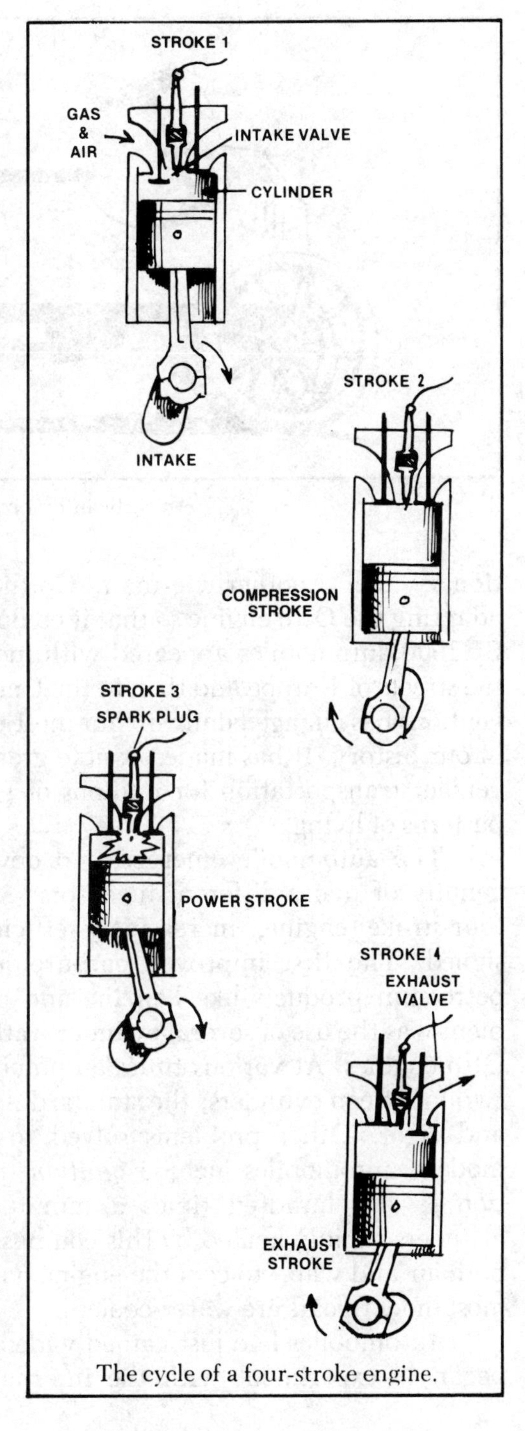

The cycle of a four-stroke engine.

An early automobile.

tionary use. Another German, Gottlieb Daimler, pioneered in adapting the Otto engine so that it could be used to power vehicles. By 1900 automobiles appeared with increasing frequency, first on the streets of Europe and then in the United States. This series of inventions has changed daily life for most people as much as any other in our history. It has made possible great industries, provided convenient transportation for millions of people and established new patterns of living.

The automobile emerged and developed because of the ingenuity of many different inventors. As an addition to the basic four-stroke engine, increasingly efficient carburetors were designed. The first improved carburetors replaced coal gas with petroleum products like benzine and gasoline. Another development was the use of several cylinders rather than the one in the first Otto engines. At various times automobile engines have had from two to sixteen cylinders; the standard numbers today are four, six, and eight. Other problems solved to achieve the efficiency of modern automobiles include *ignition systems* that cause combustion several hundred times a minute and cooling systems for cylinders rapidly heated by this combustion. Methods that employ both air and water to cool the engine have been engineered though most modern cars are water-cooled.

Automobiles had just gained wide acceptance when inventors began to experiment with the internal combustion engine as a source of power for flying machines. Flight is one of our oldest dreams but the reality of powered flight transcending the bonds of wind, air currents, and gravity belongs entirely to the twentieth century. The first successful flight in a powered aircraft was made by two Americans, Wilbur and Orville Wright, in December of 1903 at Kitty Hawk, North Carolina. They put a gasoline engine into a *glider* and this fragile contrivance flew for twelve seconds. In time for World War I (1914-1918) airplanes had been developed for use as weapons. The decades of the 1920s and 1930s saw the beginning of commercial aviation. When World War II (1939-1945) exploded air power was a major factor for victory and defeat.

The Wright brothers plane.

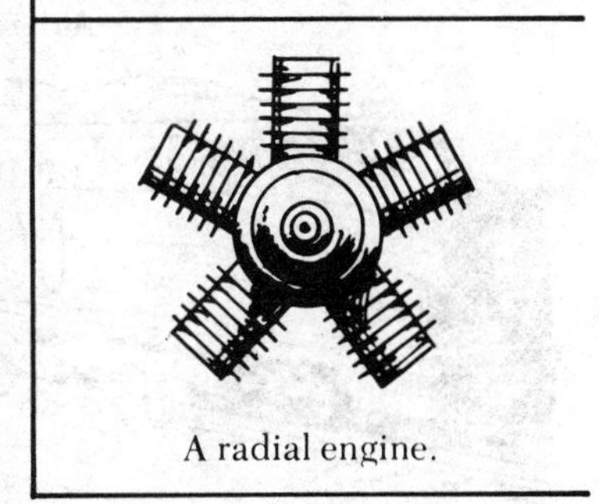

A radial engine.

Before the development of modern jet engines, to be explored in the next unit, airplanes were powered by gasoline internal combustion engines; these were light and powerful, both necessary conditions for flight. They used a *radial engine* with cylinders arranged around a central point like the spokes of a wheel. One cylinder was joined to the crank by a master connecting rod; the other cylinders were joined by hinged rods to the master connecting rod rather than to the crank. The crankshaft connected to a propeller which, as previously described, makes a helical motion that almost literally "screws" the plane through the air.

Another type of internal combustion engine is the *diesel engine*, named for its German inventor, Rudolf Diesel. In a diesel engine air is compressed to a very small proportion of its original volume; this causes the air to become so hot that combustion takes place when fuel is injected into the cylinder. Diesel engines have several advantages: they do not require a spark, they operate with cheaper fuel than other internal combustion engines, and they have a higher thermal efficiency thereby developing more power in ratio to the amount of fuel used.

Diesel engines have gained wide acceptance for many heavy-

A diesel engine.

duty vehicles, including ships, trucks, heavy equipment, and some types of passenger cars. Diesel locomotives have almost completely replaced steam engines on railroads. As an example of the complexity of modern machinery, diesel engines are used to provide power to run electric generators whose electricity is then used by the electric motors that perform the actual work on diesel locomotives!

A diesel locomotive.

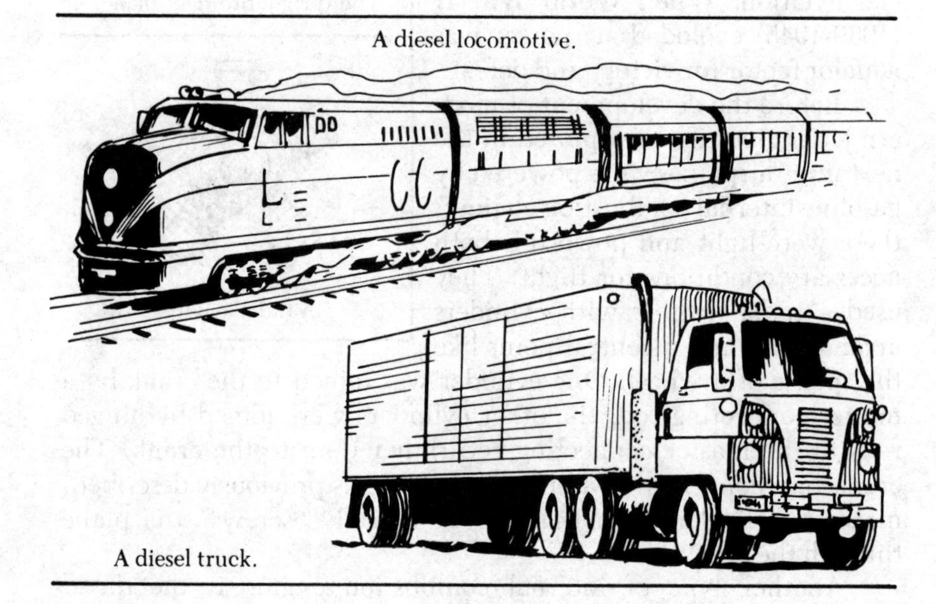
A diesel truck.

Discussion

1. Why is a steam engine sometimes called an external combustion engine? How does this indicate its difference from an internal combustion engine?

2. What were some of the early fuels used for internal combustion engines?

3. Outline the development of petroleum products in relation to development of the internal combustion engine.

4. Who invented the first workable internal combustion engine?

5. Describe the working of a four-stroke engine.

6. What do the carburetor, the spark plugs, and the valves do in a four-stroke engine?

7. What helps the piston over its first two strokes?

8. Name another necessary component of the four-stroke engine. Why does it make only one revolution for every two of the crankshaft?

9. Was Otto's engine successful? What was its drawback?

10. Name one of the pioneers in adapting the Otto engine to transportation.

11. Discuss the impact of the automobile.

12. Discuss some of the new developments in automobiles.

13. What other vehicle developed at about the time that automobiles became popular?

14. When, where, and by whom was the first successful flight in a powered aircraft taken? How long did that flight last?

15. Discuss the importance of powered flight.

16. What are two necessary conditions for powered aircraft engines? What kind of engine meets these requirements?

17. What is a radial engine? How are the cylinders attached to the crankshaft?

18. Who was Rudolf Diesel?

19. What is the principle on which a diesel engine works?

20. What are some advantages of the diesel engine?

21. What are some uses of the diesel engine?

22. How does a diesel locomotive work?

Review

A. Complete the following sentences with the appropriate word or phrase.

1. ________________ is a word that means fire or burning.

2. In a ________________ engine the piston makes two upward and two downward movements.

3. The first successful internal combustion engine, the ________________ engine, was invented by a German.

4. Gasoline is changed into a vapor and mixed with air in a ________________.

5. A ________________ stores energy that is used to help the piston make the first two strokes in a four-stroke cycle.

6. A ________________, which controls the opening and closing of the valves in the cylinder, makes only one revolution to every two of the crankshaft.

7. In an internal combustion engine, a fire or combustion takes place inside the ________________ of the engine.

8. ________________, a German inventor, was a pioneer in adapting the internal combustion engine for transportation in the form of the automobile.

9. The ______________ system causes combustion in car cylinders several hundred times a minute.

10. A ______________ is an aircraft that flies without power as a result of the action of air currents.

11. Aircraft powered by internal combustion engines usually had ______________ engines with the cylinders arranged like the spokes in a wheel.

12. The propeller of an aircraft makes a ______________ motion.

13. An internal combustion engine that compresses air until it becomes so hot that an explosion takes place when fuel is injected into the cylinder is known as a ______________ engine.

B. Label the parts in this diagram of the internal combustion engine. Then explain briefly what function each one of these performs.

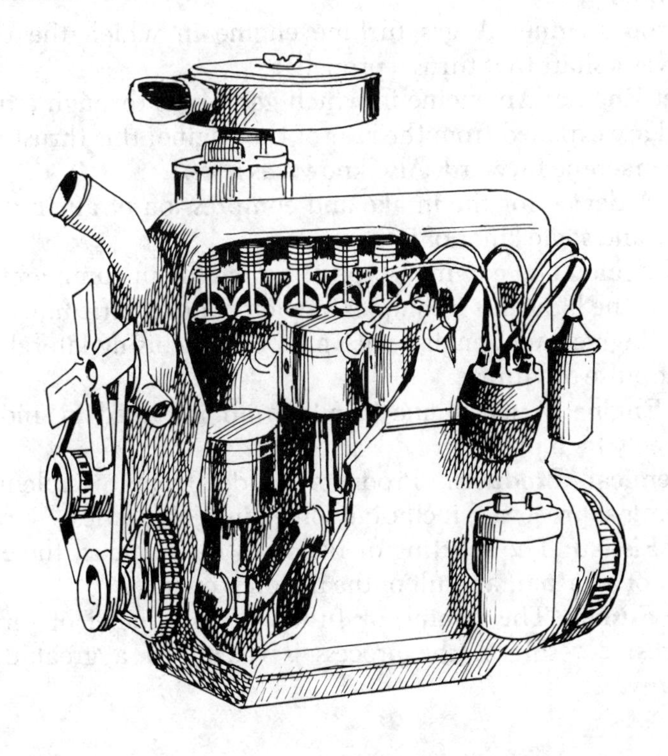

UNIT EIGHT
GAS TURBINES AND OTHER TYPES OF ENGINES

Special Terms

Gas Turbine Engine: An internal combustion engine in which combustion drives a turbine with blades similar to those of a steam turbine.

Turboprop Engine: A gas turbine engine in which the turbine drives a shaft that turns a propeller.

Turbojet Engine: An engine in which gases pass through a turbine and are expelled from the rear of the engine; this thrust pushes the machine forward. Also known as a *jet*.

Blower: A device for the intake and compression of air in gas turbine and some kinds of jet engines.

Fanjet Engine: The common type of jet engine in commercial aircraft; the blower is a complex version of an electric fan.

Pulsejet Engine: A jet engine with an air intake using lateral valves that pulse or vibrate.

Ramjet Engine: A jet engine in which air is forced in under extremely high pressure.

Petrochemical Products: Products made from petroleum by chemical processes, including some kinds of plastics.

Nuclear Fission: The splitting or fission of the nucleus, the central part of an atom; a result of the fission is energy.

Nuclear Fusion: The joining or fusion of the nuclei of different atoms; a result of the process is release of a great deal of energy.

Hot-air Engine: An engine using heated air to push down a piston; also known as the *Stirling engine.*

Rotary Engine: An internal combustion engine producing rotary instead of reciprocating motion; the best known type is called the *Wankel engine* after its inventor.

Rotor: A machine component which revolves, thereby producing rotary motion.

Vocabulary Practice

1. What is a *gas turbine engine*?
2. What is a *turboprop engine*?
3. What is a *turbojet engine*?
4. What is the purpose of a *blower*?
5. What is the characteristic of a *fanjet* which has given it its name?
6. What is the characteristic of a *pulsejet* which has given it its name?
7. What is the characteristic of a *ramjet* which has given it its name?
8. What are *petrochemical products*?
9. Describe the difference between *nuclear fission* and *nuclear fusion*.
10. What is a *hot-air engine*? What else is it called?
11. What is a *rotary engine*? What is the best known type called?
12. Describe a *rotor*.

Gas Turbines and Other Types of Engines

The idea of an internal combustion engine to drive a turbine, rather than pistons, evolved on paper as long ago as 1791 but it needed modern technology to make such an engine possible. The problem was that the blades of a turbine could not withstand the great heat resulting from the combustion in such an engine. Now new alloys or mixtures of metals, as well as some ceramics and crystals that do not fail or disintegrate at high degrees of heat, have been developed.

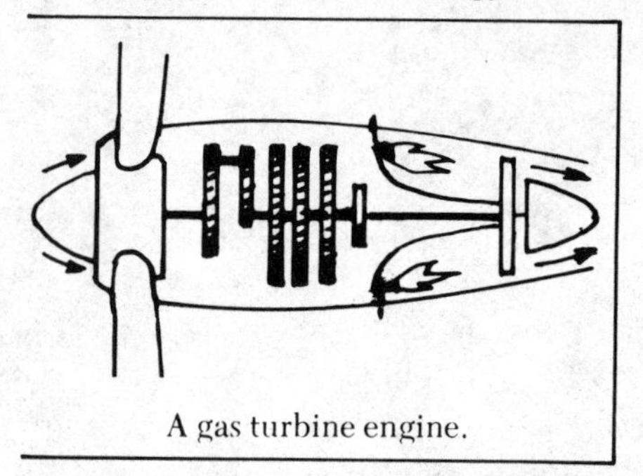

A gas turbine engine.

In a basic *gas turbine engine* air is taken in and compressed until it becomes extremely hot. The compressed air is then mixed with fuel, usually kerosene, which ignites. The expanding gases caused by the combustion cause the turbine to turn. The turbine then turns a shaft which performs the actual work. In a *turboprop engine* for aircraft that shaft turns a propeller.

Experiments to adapt gas turbines for other forms of transportation have not been entirely successful. A major drawback, especially in view of today's energy crisis, is the necessity for large amounts of fuel; the combustion is continuous in gas turbines rather than intermittent as in piston engines.

The first successful *turbojet engine* was designed by Frank Whittle, an English officer in the Royal Air Force. Jets were in use as military aircraft before the end of World War II but they did not come into commercial use until the 1950s. They have enormously increased the speed, range, and size of modern airplanes. Some types of turbojets can propel a plane at speeds faster than sound. The use of engines at supersonic speeds is one of the more controversial subjects of our time.

In a turbojet engine air is taken in by a *blower* that operates on a shaft from a turbine; the waste gases are expelled from the rear of the engine at an extremely high rate of speed. The plane is driven forward by a practical illustration of Newton's Third Law of Motion: for every action there is an equal and opposite reaction;

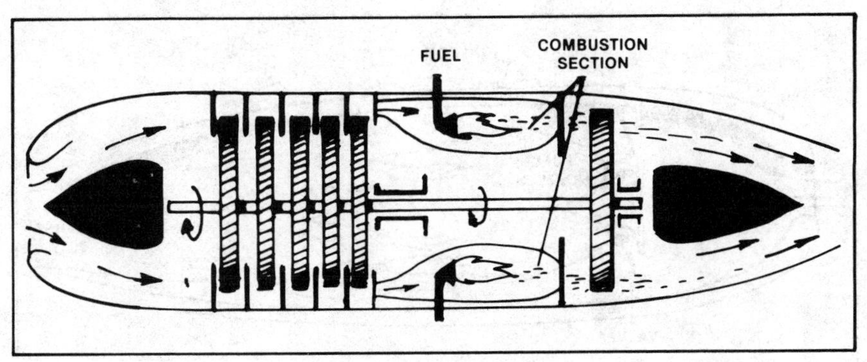

A turbojet engine.

therefore the thrust of the gases backward pushes the plane forward.

The type of turbojet in common commercial use is the *fanjet*. The intake blower is in effect a highly sophisticated version of the everyday electric fan. Two other types, used for military aircraft, are the *pulsejet* and the *ramjet*. The pulsejet, used by the German V-1 bombs to attack London during World War II, has lateral intake valves that produce a pulsing or vibrating movement; air pressure opens the valves, the explosions of fuel close them and push against them to provide forward propulsion; no turbine is necessary in this type of engine. In the ramjet, air is rammed or forced into the intake at such pressure that no blower or turbine is necessary, only a means of injecting the fuel.

A word about the energy crisis: the world's supply of petroleum was created millions of years ago and it cannot be replaced or renewed in our time. Estimates vary on how long the supply will last but according to some experts it may not be much more than thirty years at the present rate of consumption. Automobiles, diesels, and jets use enormous amounts of fuel derived from petroleum as do households and power plants that produce electricity. Petroleum is also the basis for *petrochemical products* including many of today's plastics, fertilizers, and insecticides.

Therefore there is a mounting interest in engines that do not use petroleum as fuel. Some power plants are already converting from oil to coal, but while coal is in much greater supply than petroleum it is another nonrenewable energy source which will eventually be exhausted. Experiments are under way to harness such energy sources as the wind, the tides, and the sun. *Nuclear fu-*

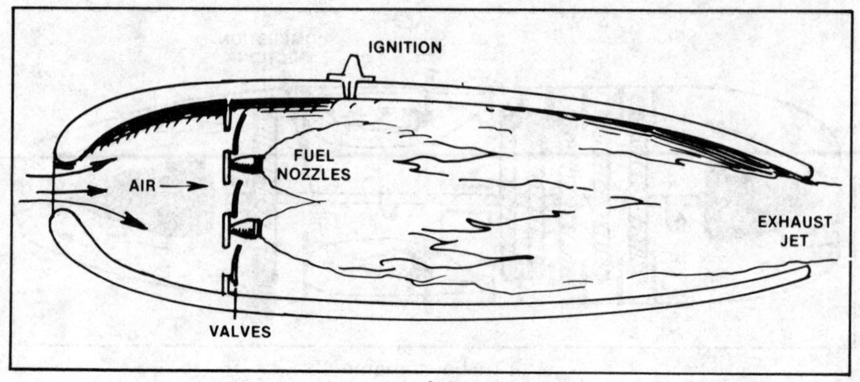

A pulsejet.

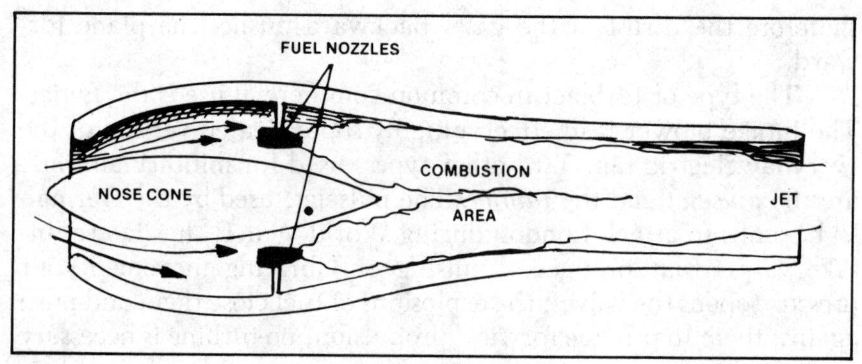

A ramjet.

sion—the release of energy when atoms join together—is being explored as a safer alternative to *nuclear fission* with its hazardous by-products of radioactive wastes that pose a serious threat to the environment and to human life. The difficulty with fusion is that it requires an enormously high degree of heat to start the reaction; to date it has not been possible to generate that much heat even under laboratory conditions.

There is much interest today in *hot-air* and *rotary engines*. The hot-air engine has a long history: a Scotsman, Robert Stirling, built one in 1827 so the hot-air engine is often called the Stirling engine. Then John Ericsson, a Swede who became a citizen of the United States (he is best remembered as the designer of the ironclad ship *Monitor* during the Civil War), built and marketed thousands of hot-air engines. The Stirling engine has two cylinders, one of which compresses air; when the air is heated it expands and pushes down a piston in the other cylinder. Engineers today are working to improve the basic Stirling engine and this offers a promise of greater fuel efficiency.

A rotary engine should more properly be called a rotating internal combustion engine. Instead of the reciprocating motion of pistons, a rotary motion is produced directly. The best-known rotary engine is the Wankel engine, named for its German inventor, Felix Wankel. The combustion in the Wankel engine turns a *rotor* that is triangular, though the outer edges are curved outward or convex. It produces almost no vibration because it has fewer parts; for this reason it is cheaper to manufacture but its fuel efficiency is still in question. Automobiles with Wankel engines use gasoline as fuel since that is what is available; if other fuels become commercially feasible the Wankel engine may be more economical than it is at present. Other inventors have produced other types of rotating combustion engines which offer interesting possibilities in experimental models.

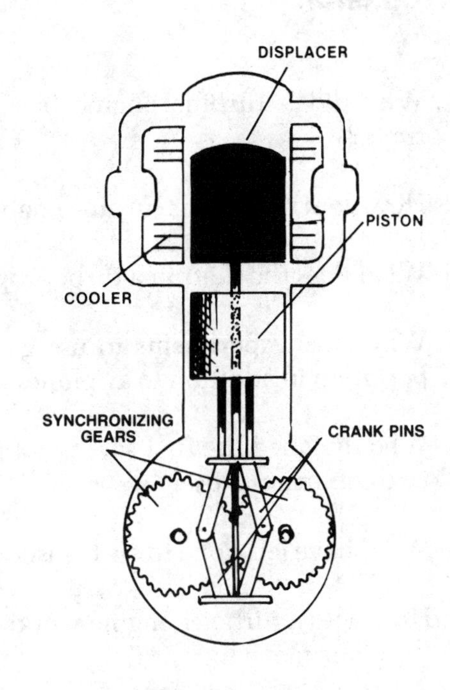

The Stirling engine.

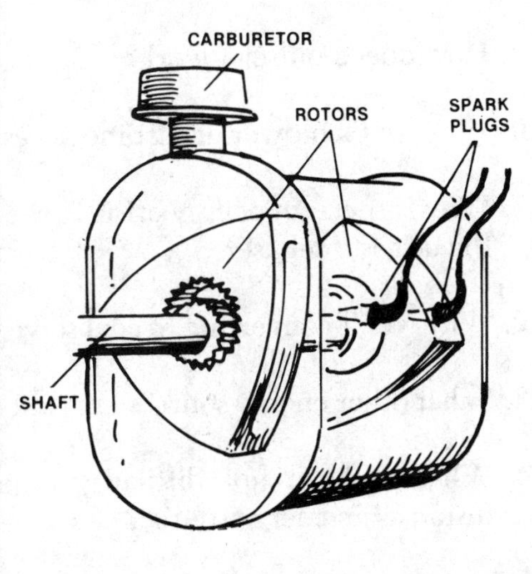

The Wankel engine.

Discussion

1. Why did a turbine engine become possible only in modern times?

2. How does a basic gas turbine engine work?

3. What does the shaft in a turboprop engine turn?

4. Why have experiments to use gas turbines for forms of transportation in addition to airplanes not been successful?

5. Who designed the first successful jet engine? When did it come into commercial use?

6. What have jets done to air transportation?

7. How does a turbojet engine work? How do the jet engines make the plane move forward?

8. What kind of turbojet is in common commercial use? Describe its blower.

9. How does a pulsejet work?

10. Why isn't a blower or turbine necessary in a ramjet?

11. Why is there an energy crisis in the world today? Name some of the largest fuel users.

12. Why won't converting to coal solve the basic energy crisis?

13. What other energy sources are experimental?

14. What is the major difficulty in the development of nuclear fusion as an energy source?

15. What kind of engine did Robert Stirling build? When did he build it?

16. Who was John Ericsson and what was his connection with hot-air engines?

17. What is the principle on which the Stirling engine works?

18. What kind of motion is produced by a rotary engine? How does this differ from the usual type of internal combustion engine?

19. Name the best-known type of rotary engine. How does it work?

20. Describe some advantages of the rotary engine.

21. What would increase the fuel efficiency of the Wankel engine?

22. Are there other rotating combustion engines? Discuss your answer.

Review

A. Complete the following sentences with the appropriate word or phrase.

1. In a gas turbine engine the combustion drives the blades of a turbine instead of ________________.

2. Some airplanes have engines in which a shaft driven by a turbine turns a ________________.

3. In a ________________ engine gases expelled from the rear of the engine provide forward propulsion.

4. Newton's Third Law of Motion states that for every action there is an ________________ and ________________ reaction.

5. Air is taken in and compressed by a ________________ in a turbojet engine.

6. A __________ is the type of jet engine in common use for commercial aircraft.

7. A __________ has lateral intake valves that vibrate.

8. In a __________ air is forced into the engine under extremely high pressure.

9. Most plastics are __________ products.

10. Nuclear __________ refers to splitting the nucleus of an atom; nuclear __________ indicates that the nuclei of atoms are joining together.

11. The Stirling engine is a __________ engine.

12. The Wankel engine produces __________ motion rather than __________ motion.

B. Identify the engines in each of the following drawings. Explain briefly how each one operates.

1.

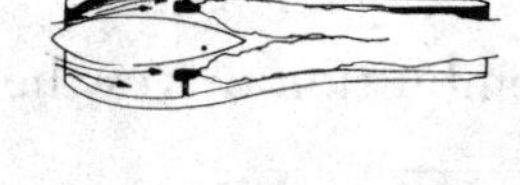

2.

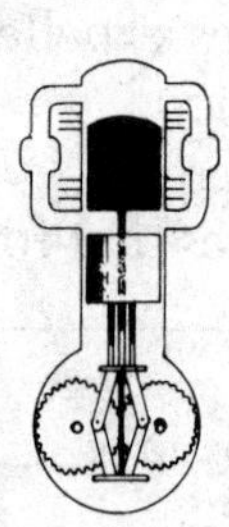

3. 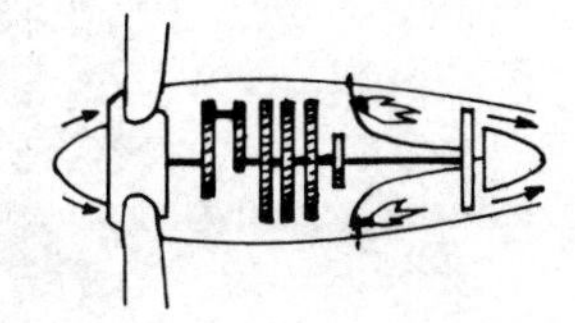

4. 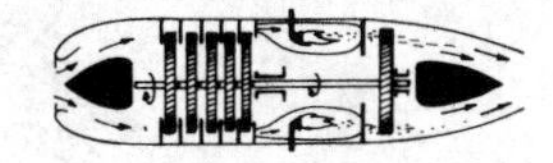

5. 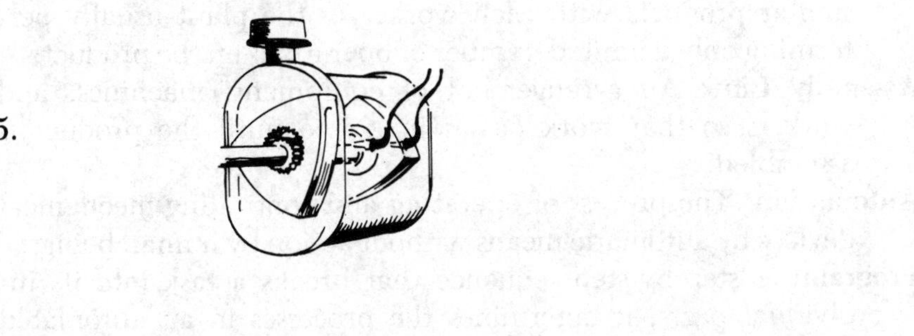

6. 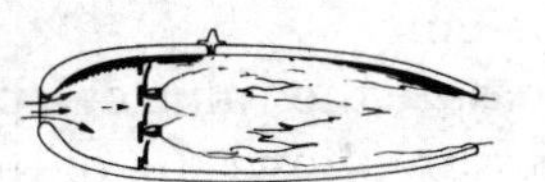

UNIT NINE
INDUSTRIAL ENGINEERING AND AUTOMATION

Special Terms

Industrial Engineering: The subdivision of mechanical engineering that deals with the use of machines in industrial or manufacturing processes.

Mass Production: Manufacturing of large quantities of exactly similar products with each worker in the plant usually performing only a limited number of operations on the product.

Assembly Line: An arrangement of equipment, machines, and workers so that work passes in a line until the product is assembled.

Automation: The process of operating and controlling mechanical devices by automatic means without action by human beings.

Program: A step-by-step sequence that breaks a task into its individual parts; it determines the processes in an automated system.

Action Elements: The components of an automated system that perform the actual work.

Mechanical Handling Devices: Another term for the action elements in an automated system.

Sensing Devices: Devices that measure the value of a physical quantity such as temperature, pressure, flowrate, or thickness.

Feedback: Information is sent from the sensing device to an instrument where it is compared with a reference value to generate an error signal; the return of this error signal to control the process is known as feedback.

Decision Element: The part of an instrument that compares the information from the sensor with the reference value to generate the error signal.

Control Element: The part of an automated system that carries out the instructions given by the decision element.

Vocabulary Practice

1. What does *industrial engineering* deal with?
2. What is *mass production*?
3. Describe an *assembly line.*
4. Define the term *automation.*
5. What is a *program*?
6. What are *action elements* in an automated system? What is another term for them?
7. What are *sensing devices* in an automated system? What is another term for them?
8. What does the *decision element* of an automated system do?
9. What does the *control element* of an automated system do?

Industrial Engineering and Automation

One distinction between a mechanical engineer and an *industrial engineer* is that the former deals with individual machines while the latter deals with machines in combination as part of a system. Industrial engineering is concerned with problems such as manufacturing processes and plant layout.

Industrial engineers must make the most efficient use of plant and equipment to achieve the highest possible degree of productivity. Originally this was conceived entirely in the mechanical terms of what machines could do and how they should be arranged. Now it is known that the effectiveness of the workers in the system must also be considered. The industrial engineer is therefore often involved in labor relations.

Industrial engineering in practice if not in name was born at the beginning of the machine age. People like Newcomen, Watt, and Pickard had to be involved not only in the invention of machines but in their application and installation. Throughout the eighteenth and nineteenth centuries the use of machines for all kinds of manufacturing (beginning in most countries with textiles) multiplied many times. We have mentioned the belt drives common in factories where steam engines powered other machines. These dangerous belts are an example of the problems with which industrial engineers dealt and the solutions they evolved.

A major advance in twentieth century manufacturing was the development of *mass production* techniques. Mass production refers to manufacturing processes in which an *assembly line*, usually a conveyor belt, moves the product to stations where each worker performs a limited number of operations until the product is assembled. In the automobile assembly plant such systems have reached a highly-developed form. A complex system of conveyer belts and chain drives moves car parts to workers who perform the thousands of necessary assembling tasks.

Mass production increases efficiency and productivity to a point beyond which the monotony of repeating an operation over and over slows down the workers. Many ways have been tried to increase productivity on assembly lines: some of them are as superficial as piping music into the plant or painting the industrial apparatus in bright colors; others entail giving workers more variety in their tasks and more responsibility for the product. Some automobile companies have experimented with giving individual workers complete responsibility for assembling an entire car; this obviously requires an extraordinarily high degree of skill.

These human factors are important considerations for industrial engineers who must try to balance an efficient system of manufacturing with the complex needs of workers.

Another factor for the industrial engineer to consider is

whether each manufacturing process can be automated in whole or in part. *Automation* is a word coined in the 1940s to describe processes by which machines do tasks previously performed by people. The word was new but the idea was not. We know of the advance in the development of steam engines that produced automatic valves. Long before that, during the Middle Ages, windmills had been made to turn by taking advantage of changes in the wind by means of devices that worked automatically. A major development in textile manufacturing was the loom developed in 1801 by Joseph-Marie Jacquard, a French inventor. Intricate patterns woven into the cloth were controlled by steel cards with holes which were forerunners of the modern computer punch card.

We now use the term automation for specific techniques combined to operate automatically in a complete system. These techniques are possible because of electronic devices, most of which have come into use in the last thirty years. They include *program*, *action*, *sensing* or *feedback*, *decision*, and *control elements* as components of a complete system.

The program elements determine what the system does and the step-by-step manner in which it works to produce the desired result. A program is a step-by-step sequence that breaks a task into its individual parts. Some steps in an industrial automation program direct other parts of the system when and how to carry out their jobs.

The action elements are those which do the actual work. They may carry or convey materials to specific places at specific times or they may perform operations on the materials. The term *mechanical handling device* is also used for the action elements.

Perhaps the most important part of an automated system is sensing or feedback. Sensing devices automatically check on parts of the manufacturing process such as the degree of heat or the thickness of a sheet of steel or paper. This is called feedback because the instruments return or feed back this information to the central system control.

The decision element is used to compare what *is* going on in the system with what *should* be going on; it receives information from the sensing devices and makes decisions necessary to maintain the system correctly. If some action is necessary the decision element can give instructions or commands to the system.

The control element consists of devices to carry out the commands of the decision element. They may be many kinds of devices: valves that open or close, switches that control the flow of electricity, or regulators that change the voltage in various machines; they make the necessary corrections or adjustments to keep the system in conformity with its program.

Automation was first applied to industry in continuous-process manufacturing such as refining petroleum, making petrochemicals, and refining steel. A later development was computer-controlled automation of assembly line manufacturing, especially those in which quality control was an important factor.

An industrial engineer working with automated systems is part of a team. Many components of the system, such as computers, are electronic devices so electronic engineers and technicians are also involved. Many of the industries in which automation has proved particularly suitable—chemicals, papermaking, metals processing—involve chemical processes, so there may be chemical engineers at work too. An industrial engineer with expertise in all these fields may become a systems engineer for automation projects thereby coordinating the activities of all the members of the team.

Discussion

1. Name a distinction between a mechanical and an industrial engineer.

2. What kinds of problems does industrial engineering deal with?

3. How do industrial engineers try to use plants and equipment?

4. What are some factors the industrial engineer must consider?

5. When did industrial engineering get started in fact if not in name? Give examples of early efforts that can be considered industrial engineering.

6. Name a major development in manufacturing in the twentieth century. What techniques does this involve?

7. How is mass production often exemplified by the assembly of automobiles?

8. Discuss efficiency and productivity in mass production.

9. Describe some experiments to increase productivity on assembly lines.

10. How is the industrial engineer involved in this problem?

11. When and why was the word *automation* coined?

12. Give some examples of automation that were in use before the word itself was created.

13. Describe the forerunner of the modern computer punch card.

14. What are some elements of an automated system? What makes them possible?

15. What is a program? What does it do in an automated system?

16. Name two terms used to describe the elements which do the actual work. What are some jobs these elements may do?

17. What are some of the things sensing devices do?

18. How do sensing devices act on the information they receive? Why is the process sometimes called feedback?

19. What is the function of the decision element? What can it do?

20. What does the control element consist of? What can these devices do? What is their purpose?

21. To what kinds of industries was automation first applied?

22. What was a later development in industrial automation?

23. What skills are necessary on a team involved in industrial automation? Why are people with these various skills involved?

24. What do we call an industrial engineer with a number of different automation skills?

Review

A. Complete the following sentences with the appropriate word or phrase.

1. ______________ engineering is a branch of mechanical engineering that is involved primarily with manufacturing processes.

2. When large numbers of products that are exactly similar, like automobiles, are being manufactured ______________ techniques will probably be used.

3. An ______________ consists of conveyer belts or chain drives that deliver products and materials to workers at particular times during the manufacturing process.

4. ______________ involves systems for operating or controlling machines mechanically rather than by the action of human beings.

5. A step-by-step sequence that breaks a job into individual parts is a ______________

6. ______________ elements perform the actual work in an automated system.

7. ______________ devices may convey materials to specific places at specific times or may perform operations on the materials.

8. ______________ devices check on conditions such as heat, thickness, and weight in an automated system.

9. The process that returns information to the control is called ______________.

10. The ______________ element in an automated system can compare what is happening with what should be happening

and then give instructions so that the system will function according to its program.

11. The devices such as valves, switches, and voltage regulators that carry out instructions of the decision element are known collectively as the ________________ element.

B. Make a diagram of the way in which you think the different elements in an automated system work in relation to each other. Explain briefly the function of each element in the system.

INDEX
OF SPECIAL TERMS

NOTES

NOTES

NOTES